Student Friends in Ch

Volume 1

Learn to Love Your Moles

John Brockington

BSc., C.Chem., MRSC

Curriculum Press

Published by The Curriculum Press
10 St. Paul's Square,
Birmingham B3 1QU

First published 1998
Reprinted 1998

ISBN   0   9532341   0 X

Cover design by Mark Smith and Sue Miller

Printed by Alphagraphics Ltd, Birmingham

Learn to Love Your Moles

TABLE OF CONTENTS

Page

An Open Letter

Dear Student,

Are you one of those people who seldom has any difficulty with chemistry calculations? If so, pat yourself on the back. (Better still, get your best friend to do it for you - it's more fun!) Or do you, like so many chemistry students, dread the word "calculate"? Either way, I hope that this book will be of immense help to you. The consequences of not coping properly with calculations and formulae, yields and volumetric analysis are invariably serious, ranging from under-achievement to the abandonment of chemistry altogether. Even a one grade slippage can be catastrophic; say a 'C' instead of a 'B, because so many professions (notably medicine) stipulate a high grade pass as an essential entry requirement.

Firstly let me reassure you about the maths. You <u>can</u> do it. Apart from having to be able to do simple proportion calculations and to solve equations by cross-multiplication - two techniques that are covered in a few pages in this book - chemistry students are not required to have any mathematical skills at all. Difficulties stem from their inability to write the formulae of compounds and with this in mind I have devoted *Chapter 1* of this book purely to formulae, to give you a sound foundation for the calculations.

However, I believe that the main problem is that, despite being a major 'A' level topic, quantitative chemistry is given little prominence in most textbooks. Some virtually ignore it, while others dismiss it in a brief chapter. (None of which seems to deter the Boards from asking some rather searching examination questions!) All too often, teachers battling against the clock and textbook authors struggling with the constraints of space are unable to do justice to what, in reality, is a complex and extensive topic, leaving students to 'pick it up as they go along'. Not surprisingly, many students feel that they cannot cope, so that schools and colleges are then faced with the prospect of having to arrange 'catching-up classes'; sometimes perilously close to the examination. If you have to attend classes of this kind, or if you feel you *need* them, you should find this book extremely useful.

As you will realise from the title, all calculations in this book are presented in terms of moles - not 'atomic mass units', which are now out of date. Do not worry about defining a mole until you are well into your 'A' level course. You can use it quite happily if you simply regard it as an *amount of substance* which is essentially the relative molecular mass expressed in grams. Converting grams to moles (or vice versa) is easy, as we shall see in *Chapter 2*, and once you can do this the door is wide open to a whole range of calculations. Think of moles as your friends, helping you to do calculations which, on any other basis, would be much more difficult. Bear in mind, too, that working in moles is a modern method and, above all else, *is the way in which examiners expect you to work!*

I do hope that you will enjoy this little book as much as I have enjoyed writing it. I have always believed that chemistry should be fun, and with this in mind I have written the text in a highly informal style, even to the extent of including a few teacher jokes. Do accept my apologies if you find them too excruciating! Finally, should you encounter any errors or obscurities, please let me know. Colleagues (particularly Kevin Byrne, Cath Brown and Peter Stamper) and students at Abbey College, Birmingham, to whom I must acknowledge a real debt of gratitude, have read through the text and suggested improvements, but any comments from *you* would be equally welcome.

Yours sincerely,

John Brockington   Birmingham, November 1997

Chapter 1

FORMULAE OF COMPOUNDS

Time and again, when students have complained that they cannot do chemical calculations, I have found that the root cause is that they do not know the formulae of compounds. So let me be brutally frank: you cannot make any progress at all unless you can write formulae. And they must be correct! It is not good enough, for example, to write the formula of sodium carbonate as $NaCO_3$ (instead of Na_2CO_3) or sodium chloride as $NaCl_2$ (instead of $NaCl$). If you cannot write the formulae of compounds, then you cannot write correctly balanced equations; and if you cannot write equations you cannot do calculations on reacting masses, volumetric analysis or, indeed, almost anything else. So much for the bad news! Now for the good news, which is that most students, once they have mastered formulae, can generally do chemical calculations on a mole basis without undue difficulty.

Chemical compounds fall into two categories, namely covalent and ionic. Covalent compounds consist of *molecules*, i.e. two or more atoms joined together by covalent bonds. (They are sometimes called 'molecular compounds'.) Ionic (or 'electrovalent') compounds, by contrast, *do not contain molecules.* Instead, they consist of *ions.* An ion, by definition, is an electrically charged atom or group of atoms. There is a huge difference between the physical properties of the two sorts. Whereas ionic compounds (e.g. sodium chloride) are invariably crystalline solids with high melting points (>500 °C), covalent compounds (e.g. water) are gases, liquids or low melting point solids. (Melting points are generally <300 °C.) It is a simple matter, in the laboratory, to decide whether a particular substance is ionic or covalent. We just melt it, insert a couple of inert electrodes, apply an electrical potential difference (i.e. a voltage) and see whether or not a current flows. If it does, there must be ions present to carry the current; if, on the other hand, no current flows, there can be no ions present; and, if there are no ions, there must be molecules.

Formulae Of Covalent Compounds

Many covalent compounds are organic; their formulae can generally be predicted from their names according to a set of well known rules. Space, however, obliges us to concentrate on inorganic compounds only.

Binary compounds
A 'binary compound' is one which is derived from two elements only. Some of these have trivial names which are unrelated to formulae, e.g.

water, H_2O ammonia, NH_3 methane, CH_4

Others have systematic names which provide a good clue to their formulae. Just remember the meanings of what chemists call 'multiplying prefixes'. *Mono* means 1, *di* = 2, *tri* = 3, *tetra* = 4, *penta* = 5 and *hexa* = 6. Here are some examples.

carbon monoxide, CO	carbon dioxide, CO_2	
phosphorus trichloride, PCl_3	phosphorus pentachloride, PCl_5	
dinitrogen monoxide, N_2O	nitrogen monoxide, NO	nitrogen dioxide, NO_2
sulphur dioxide, SO_2	sulphur trioxide, SO_3	

Acids

Without doubt, some of the most important covalent compounds are acids. Hydrochloric acid is a solution in water of a gas called hydrogen chloride; both hydrochloric acid and hydrogen chloride have the formula HCl. If we wish to distinguish between them we use *state symbols*; HCl(aq) stands for hydrochloric acid and HCl(g) for hydrogen chloride. There are four state symbols in common use:

(g) = gas   (l) = liquid   (s) = solid   (aq) = aqueous

Related substances are as follows:

HF(g)   hydrogen fluoride   HF(aq)   hydrofluoric acid
HBr(g)   hydrogen bromide   HBr(aq)   hydrobromic acid
HI(g)   hydrogen iodide   HI(aq)   hydroiodic acid

You should also learn the formulae of the following acids:

nitrous acid, HNO_2 nitric acid, HNO_3 carbonic acid, H_2CO_3
sulphurous acid, H_2SO_3 sulphuric acid, H_2SO_4 phosphoric acid, H_3PO_4

Notice that an acid whose name ends in '—ous' has a relatively low oxygen content, while the higher acid (i.e. one of higher oxygen content) has a name ending in ' —ic'.

Formulae Of Ionic Compounds

All ionic compounds consist of positively charged ions called *cations*, because they travel to the cathode on electrolysis, and negatively charged ions called *anions* because they move towards the anode. Despite the fact that they contain charged ions, *ionic compounds as a whole are always electrically neutral, because the number of positive charges from the cations is exactly equal to the number of negative charges from the anions.*

Ionic compounds can be classified as *bases* and *salts*. A 'base' is a compound which can neutralise an acid to produce a 'salt'. We shall consider first bases and then salts.

Ionic bases

These compounds are metal oxides and hydroxides. The oxide ion has a double negative charge and is written O^{2-}. The hydroxide ion has a single negative charge and is written OH^-. It is an example of a *covalent ion*, so-called because the oxygen and hydrogen atoms are joined together by a covalent bond. (In contrast, the oxide ion is a *simple ion*.)

Although the anion is always one or other of these two, there are many possible metal cations. They may carry charges of 1+, 2+ or 3+. Ions from metals in Groups 1, 2 and 3 of the Periodic Table have charges which are equal to their Group numbers:

Group 1 Li^+ Na^+ K^+ Rb^+ Cs^+
Group 2 Mg^{2+} Ca^{2+} Sr^{2+} Ba^{2+}
Group 3 Al^{3+}

Transition elements (those in the middle of the Periodic Table) may give ions M^+, M^{2+} or M^{3+}. Some give more than one type of ion, and it is very important not to get confused between them. Iron, for example, gives the iron(II) ion, Fe^{2+}, and the iron(III) ion, Fe^{3+}. Here are some others:

Cr^{3+}, chromium(III) ion Co^{2+}, cobalt(II) ion Cu^+, copper(I) ion
Cu^{2+}, copper(II) ion Ag^+, silver ion Zn^{2+}, zinc ion*

* Strictly, zinc is not classified as a transition element.

When writing formulae, the essential job is to make sure that the electrical charges on the cations and anions cancel each other out. Always remember - the compound as a whole is electrically neutral. Begin by writing down the formulae of the cation and anion, e.g. for sodium hydroxide, write down Na^+ and OH^-. Then ask yourself, "What is the ionic ratio?" Here, it is 1:1, so we could write the formula as $Na^+ OH^-$. However, it is conventional to omit the charges and just write NaOH. The snag with this is that it misleads some people into thinking that sodium hydroxide consists of NaOH molecules; so we must always bear in mind that the formula NaOH is an abbreviated form of $Na^+ OH^-$.

For sodium oxide, we must begin by writing $Na^+ O^{2-}$. Clearly, the algebraic sum of the charges, as things stand, is not zero; we need another positive charge, from another sodium ion. So the ionic ratio becomes 2:1, and the formula is $Na^+ Na^+ O^{2-}$, conventionally written as Na_2O. Notice carefully the subscript 2, written to the right of the sodium ion. **We do not write 2NaO, because a 2 placed here would symbolise NaO + NaO.**

In some cases, brackets are needed. Let's try iron(III) hydroxide, composed of iron(III) ions, Fe^{3+}, and hydroxide ions, OH^-. Clearly, three OH^- ions are needed for every one Fe^{3+} to give electrical neutrality, so we could write $Fe^{3+} OH^- OH^- OH^-$, which is essentially correct but clumsy. $Fe^{3+} (OH^-)_3$ is neater; leaving out the charges (in accordance with convention) gives the accepted formula, $Fe(OH)_3$. Brackets are needed because, without them, the 3 would multiply only the H and not the O. *Everything inside the brackets is multiplied by the subscript number.*

In tough cases there is a short cut which you might find useful. Consider aluminium oxide, built up of Al^{3+} and O^{2-} ions. What is the ionic ratio? We *could* proceed by trial and error. Try 1:2, i.e. $Al^{3+} O^{2-} O^{2-}$. Wrong! (Too many negative charges.) Try $Al^{3+} Al^{3+} O^{2-} O^{2-}$. Wrong again! (Too many positive charges.) Try $Al^{3+} Al^{3+} O^{2-} O^{2-} O^{2-}$. Correct! We now have six positive and six negative charges (which cancel out), so the formula is $Al^{3+}_2 O^{2-}_3$, abbreviated to Al_2O_3. But it is much quicker to write down the ions, $Al^{3+} O^{2-}$, and then say that the number of cations is equal to the charge on the anion (here, 2); and the number of anions is equal to the charge on the cation (here, 3); so the formula immediately becomes Al_2O_3.

Question 1   Write down the formulae of the following bases: lithium oxide, magnesium oxide, calcium hydroxide, aluminium hydroxide, chromium(III) hydroxide, iron(II) hydroxide, iron(III) oxide, copper(I) oxide, copper(II) oxide, silver oxide. (Answers on p. 8.)

Salts
These contain a metal cation, as before, or the ammonium ion, NH_4^+, which is another example of a covalent ion. The anion may be a simple anion derived from a non-metal, the principal ones being as follows:

F^-, fluoride Cl^-, chloride Br^-, bromide I^-, iodide H^-, hydride S^{2-}, sulphide

Notice that the name always ends in ' —ide'.

Alternatively, the anion may be a covalent ion, derived from an acid when it *dissociates* (i.e. splits up into ions) in water. The following equations for dissociation are given because, in all cases, they show the link between the formula of an acid and that of its anion. Given the formula of an acid and the knowledge that when acids dissociate they give rise to hydrogen ions (H^+) in solution, it is possible to work out the formula of the anion. Just bear in mind that these equations must balance in terms of both elements *and charges*.

$$HNO_2 \rightleftharpoons H^+ + NO_2^- \quad \text{(nitrite ion)}$$

$$HNO_3 \rightleftharpoons H^+ + NO_3^- \quad \text{(nitrate ion)}$$

$$H_2SO_3 \rightleftharpoons 2H^+ + SO_3^{2-} \quad \text{(sulphite ion)}$$

$$H_2SO_4 \rightleftharpoons 2H^+ + SO_4^{2-} \quad \text{(sulphate ion)}$$

$$H_2CO_3 \rightleftharpoons 2H^+ + CO_3^{2-} \quad \text{(carbonate ion)}$$

$$H_3PO_4 \rightleftharpoons 3H^+ + PO_4^{3-} \quad \text{(phosphate ion)}$$

Notice that, where elements form more than one anion, the lower one (with less oxygen) is named '–ite', while the higher one is called '–ate'.

When writing the formulae of salts, you should apply the procedure given above for bases *exactly*. (If you can manage one, you can certainly do the other!) Try the following, check your answers with those printed below, and don't hesitate to ask your teacher about any you cannot do, or those which you have got wrong and do not understand.

Question 2   Write down the formulae of the following salts: potassium iodide, zinc nitrate, ammonium carbonate, aluminium sulphate, sodium carbonate, iron(II) sulphate, silver nitrate, barium chloride, sodium bromide, potassium nitrite, sodium sulphite, ammonium phosphate, cobalt(II) nitrate, copper(II) sulphate.

Answers to questions in this chapter

1. Li_2O, MgO, $Ca(OH)_2$, $Al(OH)_3$, $Cr(OH)_3$, $Fe(OH)_2$, Fe_2O_3, Cu_2O, CuO, Ag_2O.
2. KI, $Zn(NO_3)_2$, $(NH_4)_2CO_3$, $Al_2(SO_4)_3$, Na_2CO_3, $FeSO_4$, $AgNO_3$, $BaCl_2$, $NaBr$, KNO_2, Na_2SO_3, $(NH_4)_3PO_4$, $Co(NO_3)_2$, $CuSO_4$.

Chapter 2

RELATIVE MOLECULAR MASSES AND MOLES

Relative Molecular Masses

To find the relative molecular mass (M_r) of a substance, **look at the molecular formula and add together the relative atomic masses (A_r values) of the atoms it contains.** For example, ammonia has the molecular formula NH_3, which tells us that in a molecule of ammonia there are three atoms of hydrogen ($A_r = 1$) bonded to one of nitrogen ($A_r = 14$). Its relative molecular mass is therefore $1+1+1+14 = 17$.

For ionic compounds (those which consist of ions; not molecules) there is strictly speaking no such thing as a molecular formula. In such cases the formula, e.g. NaCl for sodium chloride, represents the ionic ratio: here, it tells you that Na^+ and Cl^- ions are present in a 1:1 ratio. However, it is still conventional to quote a relative molecular mass *as if the substance were molecular.* Thus, for sodium chloride, we say that the M_r = 23 (for Na) + 35.5 (for Cl) = 58.5. Some teachers, not surprisingly, object to this and talk about *relative formula masses* of ionic compounds, but in this book we shall stick to the international convention of using the term "relative molecular mass" for both covalent and ionic substances.

For elements (as distinct from compounds) there can be real problems, which we must sort out now. If the element is a metal, it will not exist as molecules and will not have a molecular formula or relative molecular mass. For all equation and calculation purposes, metals are regarded as atomic, i.e. they are treated as if they were composed of atoms. (In actual fact they exist as lattices of cations with a flux of electrons between them.)

If the element is a non-metal, it will probably exist as molecules and I expect you already know the molecular formulae of the commonest, e.g. H_2, N_2, O_2, Cl_2. Their relative molecular masses are calculated in the usual way, e.g. for hydrogen, M_r = 1+1 = 2; for oxygen M_r = 16+16 = 32. However, you should note carefully the following exceptions.

1   The noble gases (e.g. He, Ne, Ar) are monoatomic, i.e. they exist as individual atoms; not molecules. There can be no molecular formula or relative molecular mass.

2   For some polyatomic non-metals, notably phosphorus, sulphur and carbon, it is usual to disregard their molecular formulae (e.g. P_4 or S_8) and to treat them - rather like metals - as if they were atomic. Again, you should not bother with relative molecular masses, but use relative atomic masses instead.

3   In some calculations we are concerned, not with molecules of non-metals, but with their *atoms* covalently bonded to other atoms. In such calculations you must be careful to use the relative *atomic* masses of these elements; not their relative molecular masses.

Warnings!

1. Whenever you are calculating relative molecular masses of ionic compounds, always be on the lookout for curved brackets. Remember that everything inside the bracket is multiplied by the subscript number (on the right) outside the brackets. For example, the formula of zinc nitrate, $Zn(NO_3)_2$, is an abbreviation for $Zn^{2+} + NO_3^- + NO_3^-$, so the M_r is 65.4 for zinc + (2×14) for two nitrogen atoms + (6×16) for six oxygen atoms = 189.4.

In the absence of curved brackets, a subscript number relates only to the atom immediately before it. For example, the M_r of phosphoryl chloride, formula $POCl_3$, is 31 for phosphorus + 16 for oxygen + (3×35.5) for three chlorine atoms = 153.5. Notice that the subscript 3 qualifies only the chlorine and not the oxygen.

The presence of square brackets in the formulae of complex salts has no bearing at all on the calculation of relative molecular masses. Thus, the M_r of potassium hexacyanoferrate(II), $K_4[Fe(CN)_6]$, is (4×39) for four potassium atoms + 56 for iron + (6×12) for six carbon atoms + (6×14) for six nitrogen atoms = 368.

2. Whatever the nature of a substance, be it an element or a compound, **its formula and relative molecular mass are fixed** because they relate to that substance, no matter what reaction it is in. For sodium chloride, for example, its M_r is always 58.5. We could not look at the equation for the electrolytic decomposition of molten sodium chloride:

$$2NaCl \rightarrow 2Na + Cl_2$$

and argue that its formula has changed from NaCl to 2NaCl; therefore its relative molecular mass has changed. **This is totally untrue!** The figure 2, written to the left of NaCl, symbolises NaCl + NaCl. It is a number (sometimes referred to as a *coefficient*) used to balance the equation. It has in no way become part of the formula, which remains as it was, NaCl. The relative molecular mass therefore remains at 58.5.

Questions Calculate the relative molecular masses of the following substances. (The answers are on p. 11.) Use the following relative relative atomic masses: H = 1; C = 12; N = 14; O = 16; Na = 23; Al = 27; S = 32; K = 39; Ca = 40; Cr = 52; Cu = 63.5; I = 127.

1   Ethanoic acid, CH_3COOH
2   Calcium hydroxide, $Ca(OH)_2$ (*Hint* The formula represents $Ca^{2+} + OH^- + OH^-$.)
3   Iodine, I_2
4   Aluminium sulphate, $Al_2(SO_4)_3$
5   Copper(II) sulphate pentahydrate, $CuSO_4.5H_2O$ (*Hint* The water of crystallisation must be taken into account.)
6   Sodium thiosulphate pentahydrate, $Na_2S_2O_3.5H_2O$
7   Potassium dichromate(VI), $K_2Cr_2O_7$
8   Ammonium carbonate, $(NH_4)_2CO_3$

Moles

The definition of a *mole* is somewhat complicated, being based on the choice of the isotope carbon-12 as the basis of atomic and molecular masses. In this book we shall leave it alone until *Chapter 18*. For practical purposes it is quite sufficient to regard **a mole as an amount of substance given by the relative molecular mass in grams.** This applies to *all* compounds (both molecular and ionic) and to the molecular forms of most non-metallic elements, e.g. H_2 or Cl_2. Thus, for sodium hydroxide, NaOH, whose M_r is 40, one mole (symbol 1 mol) is 40 grams (written 40 g). *In general, to find how much one mole of a substance weighs, just work out the M_r and put 'grams' after it.*

As we saw earlier, certain elements do not have relative molecular masses. This applies to metallic elements (e.g. Na or Fe), noble gases (e.g. He or Ne), some polyatomic non-metals (e.g. S or C) and atoms of non-metals when they are chemically combined with other atoms (e.g. N atoms covalently bonded to H atoms in ammonia). In all these cases, a mole is the relative *atomic* mass in grams. Thus, a mole of sodium is 23 g, a mole of sulphur is 32 g and a mole of atomic nitrogen (chemically combined in ammonia) is 14 g.

Moles to grams and *grams to moles*

Nothing could be easier! We have just seen that one mole of sodium hydroxide is 40 g. Two moles (2 mol) would be 80 g, 3 mol is 120 g, etc. Hence, to convert moles into grams, we multiply the number of moles by the M_r.

$$\textbf{GRAMS} = \textbf{MOLES} \times M_r$$

The opposite conversion is equally straightforward. Suppose we had 40 g of sodium hydroxide: this would be 1 mol. 20 g is 0.5 mol; 10 g = 0.25 mol. In general terms, to convert grams into moles, we divide the mass by the M_r.

$$\textbf{MOLES} = \frac{\textbf{GRAMS}}{M_r}$$

Despite the simplicity of these conversions, they do need to be practised. Here are a few for you to try. When you've done them, check your answers with those printed.

Questions Calculate the following, using the relative atomic masses: H = 1; N = 14; O = 16; Al = 27; S = 32; Ca = 40; Cu = 63.5.

9   The mass of 1 mol of *atomic* hydrogen.
10   The mass of 1 mol of *molecular* hydrogen.
11   The mass of 2 mol of nitrogen gas.
12   The mass of 0.5 mol of aluminium sulphate.
13   The amount (in moles) of 100 g of calcium hydroxide.
14   The amount (in moles) of 1 g of copper(II) sulphate pentahydrate.
15   Five moles of a compound weigh 292.5 g. What is its M_r?
16   Half a mole of an element has a mass of 16 g. What is the element?

Answers to questions in this chapter

1. 60   2. 74   3. 254   4. 342   5. 249.5   6. 248   7. 294   8. 96   9. 1 g
10. 2 g   11. 56 g   12. 171 g   13. 1.35 mol   14. 4.01×10^{-3} mol   15. 58.5   16. Sulphur

Chapter 3

SUBSTANCES IN SOLUTION

A *solution* is made by dissolving a solute in a solvent. Sodium chloride, for instance, dissolves in water to give a colourless solution commonly called "brine". Note that the dissolved substance (here, salt) is referred to as the *solute*, while the liquid which does the dissolving is the *solvent*. Although water is by far the commonest solvent, it is by no means the only one. Others which are sometimes used include ethanol and tetrachloromethane.

Many chemical reactions occur in solution. The question then arises, and it is very important, "How many moles of solute are there in that solution?" Before we can answer this question, we must properly understand the idea of concentration.

Concentration

If there is only a little solute, a solution is said to be *dilute*, while if there is a lot of solute it is *concentrated*. A dilute solution is commonly said to be "weak", and a concentrated one "strong", but these descriptions of solutions are no longer used in chemistry. **Do not use terms 'strong' and 'weak' in this context.**

The quantity of solute in 1 dm^3 of solution is referred to as the *concentration* of that solution. It may be quoted in either grams or moles.

i.   Mass concentration, i.e. concentration in grams per dm^3.

Whenever we prepare a solution in the laboratory, we calculate its mass concentration first. Suppose, for example, that we are making 250 cm^3 of sodium chloride solution, and have weighed out 1.503 g of NaCl crystals on an analytical balance. We should then dissolve these crystals in distilled water in a beaker, transfer the solution to a 250 cm^3 graduated flask, make up to the graduation mark with more distilled water, stopper the flask and then mix well by inverting the flask slowly several times. **Notice particularly that, to make 250 cm^3 of solution, we do *not* add 250 cm^3 of water to the crystals, because this would probably give us more than 250 cm^3 of solution.** The mass concentration of the solution would be calculated as follows.

	Mass of NaCl in 250 cm^3	= 1.503 g.
	Since 250 cm^3	= $^1/_4$ dm^3 (remember that 1 dm^3 = 1000 cm^3),
	mass of NaCl in 1 dm^3	= 1.503 × 4 = 6.012 g,
i.e.	mass concentration	= 6.012 g dm^{-3}.

ii.   Molar concentration, i.e. concentration in moles per dm^3.

We have already seen that we convert grams to moles by dividing by M_r. In exactly the same way, dividing by M_r will convert mass concentration (g dm^{-3}) to molar concentration (mol dm^{-3}).

$$\textbf{MOLAR CONCENTRATION} = \frac{\textbf{CONCENTRATION IN GRAMS PER DM}^3}{\textit{\textbf{M}}_\textit{\textbf{r}}}$$

For example, sodium chloride has an M_r of 58.5. A mass concentration of 58.5 g dm^{-3} therefore becomes a molar concentration of 58.5 ÷ 58.5 = 1 mol dm^{-3}. We could say that the NaCl solution is *one molar*, written 1 M; or we could say that its *molarity* is one. **Notice that the terms *molar concentration, concentration in mol dm^{-3}* and *molarity* all mean exactly the same thing.**

$2 \times 58.5 = 117$ g dm^{-3} of NaCl would give a 2 M solution; $58.5 \div 2 = 29.25$ g dm^{-3} of NaCl would give a 0.5 M solution, and so on. Returning to the example in paragraph (i), the molarity of the solution would be $6.012 \div 58.5 = 0.103$ M.

Actually, your calculator will tell you that $6.012 \div 58.5 = 0.1027692$, but the last figures have no chemical significance because the apparatus which we commonly use in the laboratory is not that accurate. For 'A' level chemistry it is usual to quote the answer to three (sometimes four) significant figures; that is why I've written 0.103 M.

For consolidation, try the following questions yourself. Both here and throughout the book you will find the answers at the end of the chapter. Work to three significant figures, check your answers as you go along, and never go any further unless you've got them right. Ask for help if necessary. Use the following relative atomic masses for these and other questions in this chapter: H = 1; C = 12; N = 14; O = 16; Na = 23; S = 32; Cl = 35.5; K = 39; Cr = 52; Cu = 63.5; Ag = 108; I = 127.

Questions   In questions 1 and 2, calculate the molarity of each solution.

1   Hydrochloric acid of mass concentration 30.0 g dm^{-3}.
2   Aqueous potassium iodide of mass concentration 100 g dm^{-3}.

In questions 3 to 8, calculate a) the mass concentration, and b) the molarity of each solution.

3   250 cm^3 of a solution containing 1.237 g of potassium dichromate(VI), $K_2Cr_2O_7$.
4   100 cm^3 of a salt solution containing 1.00 g of NaCl.
5   2 dm^3 of aqueous sodium hydroxide containing 320 g of NaOH.
6   50 cm^3 of aqueous sodium hydroxide containing 0.304 g of NaOH.
7   25 cm^3 of aqueous silver nitrate containing 0.25 g of $AgNO_3$.
8   750 cm^3 of aqueous copper(II) sulphate containing 12.0 g of $CuSO_4.5H_2O$.

The reverse type of calculation, i.e. the conversion of molar concentration to mass concentration, is essentially a "moles to grams" calculation. This, as we've already seen, is done by multiplying by M_r. For example, for 0.05 M sodium carbonate solution,

          molar concentration   =   0.05 mol dm^{-3},
∴   mass concentration   = 0.05×106 =   5.30 g dm^{-3}.   (106 is the M_r of Na_2CO_3)

Questions In questions 9 and 10, calculate the mass concentration of each solution.

9   0.102 M sodium hydroxide.
10   0.098 M aqueous ammonia.

"How much solid do I weigh out?"

Suppose you're in the laboratory - perhaps for an assessed practical - and you are told to prepare 250 cm³ of approximately 0.05 M sodium carbonate solution and then calculate its exact molarity. What on earth do you do? Panic? Of course, because you're only human! But when you've calmed down, just think. We have already seen that 0.05 M sodium carbonate solution requires 5.30 g dm⁻³.

250 cm³ (which is ¹/₄ dm³) requires 5.30 ÷ 4 = 1.325 g

Weighing out precisely 1.325 g on an analytical balance is a fiddling and time-consuming business which is usually unnecessary. Generally, we would weigh out approximately this mass, say 1.2-1.4 g, and then calculate its exact molarity. Suppose we actually weighed 1.356 g. Then:

$$mass\ concentration = 1.356 \times 4 = 5.424\ g\ dm^{-3},$$
$$\therefore molar\ concentration = 5.424 \div 106 = 0.0512\ M.$$

Because questions of this kind are very common, you must get a reasonable amount of practice. Here are some to get you started.

Questions In questions 11 to 14, calculate in each case how much solute must be weighed out to prepare the stated solution.

11 100 cm³ of 0.05 M sodium carbonate solution.
12 5 dm³ of 4 M sodium chloride solution.
13 250 cm³ of 0.0667 M potassium iodate(V) solution, KIO_3.
14 25 cm³ of 4 M copper(II) sulphate solution, from crystals of $CuSO_4.5H_2O$.

Moles Of Substances In Solution

We are now in a strong position to calculate how many moles of a solute are present in a solution. If you think about it, you will realise that the amount in moles of any solute in any solution depends on only two factors:

i.   the molarity of the solution.
ii. the volume of that solution.

Hence,

MOLES = MOLARITY x VOLUME IN DM ³

Because molarity has units of mol dm⁻³, *volume must have units of dm³;* otherwise the units in this equation are inconsistent and any calculation will be incorrect. You are unlikely to be asked to prove this relationship, but it is quite easy to do so if necessary, if you remember that molarity is the number of moles of solute in 1 dm³ of solution. Suppose a solution contains *n* mol of solute in a volume of V dm³. We can argue that:

if V dm^3 of solution contain n mol of solute,

then   1 dm^3 contains $n \div V$ mol,

i.e.   molarity = number of moles per dm^3 = $\dfrac{n}{V}$

$\therefore$ n = molarity $\times V$

Example What mass of potassium manganate(VII) is present in 500 cm^3 of 0.02 M KMnO$_4$ (aq)? M_r of KMnO$_4$ = 158

We must find moles first; then grams.

Moles = molarity $\times$ volume (in dm^3)

= 0.02 $\times$ 0.5 = 0.01

$\therefore$ mass = 0.01 $\times$ 158 = 1.58 g

Questions

15   What is the molarity of dilute sulphuric acid, given that 25 cm^3 of the solution contain 0.05 mol H$_2$SO$_4$?

16   What volume of 0.102 M hydrochloric acid would contain 0.05 mol HCl?

Answers to questions in this chapter

1. 0.822 M   2. 0.602 M   3. 4.95 g dm^{-3}; 0.0168 M   4. 10.0 g dm^{-3}; 0.171 M
5. 160 g dm^{-3}; 4 M   6. 6.08 g dm^{-3}; 0.152 M   7. 10 g dm^{-3}; 0.0588 M   8. 16 g dm^{-3}; 0.0641 M
9. 4.08 g dm^{-3} 10. 1.67 g dm^{-3} 11. 0.53 g   12. 1170 g   13. 3.57 g   14. 24.95 g
15. 2 M   16. 0.490 dm^3 (or 490 cm^3)

Chapter 4

HOW'S YOUR MATHS?

You may be saying to yourself, "Anyone can convert grams to moles, or vice versa. This isn't the problem with mole calculations; it's the maths later on." Or, of course, you could be saying, "Maths is no problem; it's the chemistry I don't understand." One thing is certain. You *must* be able to handle simple calculations of two sorts:

i.   simple proportion calculations,
ii.   equations arising from volumetric analysis.

The time to sort this out is *now!* So, before continuing with our systematic study, I think it would be a very good idea if we paused awhile to make absolutely sure that you can handle these two sorts of calculations.

Simple Proportion Calculations

As will be explained later (*Chapter 18*), there is a constant number of molecules in a mole. (It is, in fact, an extremely large number, 6.023×10^{23}, called the Avogadro constant.) Because of this, **the ratio in which molecules react** (as shown by a chemical equation) **is the same as the ratio in which moles react.** The equation:

$$N_2(g) + 3H_2(g) \rightarrow 2NH_3(g)$$

literally tells us that one molecule of nitrogen reacts with three molecules of hydrogen to give two molecules of ammonia. (Admittedly, there isn't a number in front of the N_2 but this is only because, according to convention, the number 1 is omitted when writing equations. If ever there isn't a number in front of a formula, you must always assume the number is 1.) Therefore, provided that complete reaction occurs, one mole of nitrogen will combine with three moles of hydrogen to give two moles of ammonia.

Example   Silver nitrate solution reacts with sodium chloride solution to give a white precipitate of silver chloride:
$$AgNO_3(aq) + NaCl(aq) \rightarrow AgCl(s) + NaNO_3(aq)$$

How many moles of $AgNO_3$ and NaCl are required to produce four moles of AgCl?

The equation shows:

1 mol $AgNO_3$ + 1 mol NaCl → 1 mol AgCl + 1 mol $NaNO_3$
∴   n mol $AgNO_3$ + n mol NaCl → n mol AgCl + n mol $NaNO_3$
where n can have any value you like. Here, n = 4; therefore the requirement is 4 mol $AgNO_3$ and 4 mol NaCl.

Question 1   Aluminium hydroxide dissolves in concentrated hydrochloric acid according to the following equation:
$$2Al(OH)_3(s) + 6HCl(aq) \rightarrow 2AlCl_3(aq) + 6H_2O(l)$$

How many moles of HCl are required, in theory, to dissolve 2.84 mol of aluminium hydroxide?

Please try this and check your answer with mine on p. 21. If you have the right answer, cut the rest of this section and move to the next one (equations arising from volumetric analysis). But, if you experience any difficulty, please read on and then attempt some other questions I've provided for practice.

Answer   Start by writing a *statement* of the information provided by the equation:

2 mol Al(OH)$_3$ need 6 mol HCl.

Notice particularly that I have *not* written:

6 mol HCl need 2 mol Al(OH)$_3$

Trivial, you may say - the two statements mean exactly the same thing. Absolutely true, but the point is that, in order to do simple proportion calculations, **the item to be calculated** (in this case, moles of HCl) **must be placed on the right hand side of your statement.**

You now need to find the amount of HCl required by 1 mol Al(OH)$_3$, so divide your whole statement by 2:

1 mol Al(OH)$_3$ needs 6 ÷ 2 = 3 mol HCl

Finally, to find the amount of HCl required by 2.84 mol Al(OH)$_3$, multiply throughout by 2.84:
2.84 mol Al(OH)$_3$ need 3 × 2.84 = 8.52 mol Al(OH)$_3$

That's all there is to it! To summarise, there are three stages.

i.   Inspect the equation and write down a statement of the mole ratio of the two substances involved in the question. **Remember that the substance whose amount you are calculating must appear on the right hand side.**
ii.   Divide your statement by whatever number appears on the left hand side. (In this case we divided by 2.)
iii.   Multiply by whatever number is required by the question. (2.84 in the above example.)

Now try the following questions yourself. They shouldn't take too long; but, if they do, you can console yourself with the thought that you need the practice. And, with practice, two good things happen. First, you improve; second, you speed up.

Always check your answers with those provided at the end of the chapter. If for any reason at all you experience difficulty, or if any of your answers differ from mine, you must ask for help, either from a friend or a teacher. **Remember that we all learn from our mistakes.** Although it is disappointing when you go wrong or get stuck - there is none of the "rosy glow" associated with getting things right - this is without doubt the way to improve. So don't try to forget about your difficulties, hoping they'll go away - because they won't! Rather, focus on them; turn them to your advantage. This is the way forward, and this is the philosophy I'd like you to adopt not just here but throughout the entire book. I can promise you - it works!

Questions

2   How many moles of hydrogen can be obtained by dissolving 3 moles of zinc in excess dilute sulphuric acid?

$$Zn(s) + H_2SO_4(aq) \rightarrow ZnSO_4(aq) + H_2(g)$$

3   How many moles of carbon are required to reduce 100 moles of iron(III) oxide in the following blast furnace reaction?

$$Fe_2O_3(s) + 3C(s) \rightarrow 2Fe(l) + 3CO(g)$$

4   How many moles of chlorine could be obtained by the electrolysis of 2.5 moles of molten sodium chloride?

$$2NaCl(l) \rightarrow 2Na(l) + Cl_2(g)$$

5   How many moles of aluminium oxide would have to be electrolysed to produce 50 moles of aluminium?

$$2Al_2O_3(l) \rightarrow 4Al(l) + 3O_2(g)$$

6   Suppose it is necessary to prepare 4.75 moles of iron(III) sulphate, $Fe_2(SO_4)_3$, by the oxidation of iron(II) sulphate, $FeSO_4$, using a solution of potassium manganate(VII), $KMnO_4$, acidified by dilute sulphuric acid:

$$2KMnO_4 + 8H_2SO_4 + 10FeSO_4 \rightarrow 2MnSO_4 + 5Fe_2(SO_4)_3 + K_2SO_4 + 8H_2O$$

Calculate the theoretical amounts (in moles) of potassium manganate(VII), sulphuric acid and iron(II) sulphate which would be required.

Equations Arising From Volumetric Analysis

In volumetric analysis we find the volume of one solution which reacts with a given volume of another. The substances in those solutions may be an acid and a base, or an oxidising agent and a reducing agent: possibly others, for various types of chemical reactions can be involved. In all cases, however, the calculation of results is essentially similar. For a "trial question" I have selected an example based on neutralisation, i.e. acid-base reaction. Please try it, *to ensure that you can cope with the maths*; not the chemistry, because we shall be looking at this in detail later on.

Question 7   25.0 cm^3 of 0.049 M sulphuric acid were neutralised by 26.9 cm^3 of a certain sodium hydroxide solution. Calculate the molarity of the latter.

The relevant equation is:

$$H_2SO_4(aq) + 2NaOH(aq) \rightarrow Na_2SO_4(aq) + 2H_2O(l)$$

This shows that the mole ratio of acid:base is 1:2, which we can write as

$$\frac{\text{moles } H_2SO_4}{\text{moles NaOH}} = \frac{1}{2}$$

(We could invert this and write instead

$$\frac{\text{moles NaOH}}{\text{moles } H_2SO_4} = \frac{2}{1}$$

Frankly, it makes no difference. The two equations are mathematically identical.)

As we saw in *Chapter 3*, the amount (in moles) of any substance in any solution is equal to its molarity (i.e. concentration in moles per dm^3) multiplied by the volume in dm^3,

i.e.   moles = molarity × volume in dm^3

Consequently, the above equation can be rewritten as

$$\frac{\text{molarity} \times \text{volume (in } dm^3) \text{ of } H_2SO_4}{\text{molarity} \times \text{volume (in } dm^3) \text{ of NaOH}} = \frac{1}{2}$$

If we substitute the numbers from the question into this equation we get

$$\frac{0.049 \times 0.025}{\text{M(NaOH)} \times 0.0269} = \frac{1}{2}$$

Notice that I have converted the volumes of both solutions from cm^3 to dm^3 by dividing by 1000. (Remember that 1 dm^3 = 1000 cm^3.) M(NaOH) stands for the molarity of the sodium hydroxide solution, which is what we have to calculate.

The 64,000 dollar question now is this: "Can you solve this equation?" Do try it, and don't forget to check your answer with mine.

Answer The method used in solving these equations is commonly called *cross-multiplication.* According to this technique, any of the numbers in the equation (or an unknown term, such as M(NaOH)) can be taken from top left to bottom right (or vice versa) or from top right to bottom left (or vice versa).

The secret of success is to ensure that the unknown term, here M(NaOH), **stands by itself on one side of the equation - on the top line.** It does not matter whether it appears on the left hand side or the right hand side. *Everything else must be on the other side of the equation.*

Here, M(NaOH) must be taken from bottom left to top right. To ensure that it stands on the right hand side by itself, the number 2 must be taken from bottom right to top left. Everything else stays put. This gives

$$\frac{0.049 \times 0.025 \times 2}{0.0269} = \text{M(NaOH)}$$

Then, of course, if you use your calculator to multiply $0.049 \times 0.025 \times 2$, and finally divide by 0.0269, you will find that the molarity of the sodium hydroxide solution, to three significant figures, is 0.0911. (The calculator reading is 0.091078. Note that the noughts, both before and immediately after the decimal point, are not taken into account in the reckoning of significant figures.)

19

Here are some further questions for practice. Remember not to worry about the chemistry at this stage; treat these only as mathematical exercises.

Question 8   25.0 cm^3 of 0.052 M sodium carbonate solution neutralised 21.6 cm^3 of hydrochloric acid. The equation is

$$Na_2CO_3(aq) + 2HCl(aq) \rightarrow 2NaCl(aq) + CO_2(g) + H_2O(l)$$

Hence,
$$\frac{\text{moles HCl}}{\text{moles Na}_2\text{CO}_3} = \frac{2}{1}$$

∴
$$\frac{\text{molarity} \times \text{volume (in dm}^3\text{) of HCl}}{\text{molarity} \times \text{volume (in dm}^3\text{) of Na}_2\text{CO}_3} = \frac{2}{1}$$

∴
$$\frac{\text{M(HCl)} \times 0.0216}{0.052 \times 0.025} = \frac{2}{1}$$

Calculate the molarity of the hydrochloric acid.

Question 9   Solid calcium hydroxide ("slaked lime") reacts with hydrochloric acid according to the equation:

$$Ca(OH)_2(s) + 2HCl(aq) \rightarrow CaCl_2(aq) + 2H_2O(l)$$

Hence:
$$\frac{\text{moles HCl}}{\text{moles Ca(OH)}_2} = \frac{2}{1}$$

∴
$$\frac{\text{molarity} \times \text{volume (in dm}^3\text{) of HCl}}{\text{moles Ca(OH)}_2} = \frac{2}{1}$$

Calculate how many moles of slaked lime would have to be used to neutralise 1000 dm^3 of 9 M hydrochloric acid.

Question 10   Ethanedioic acid, $H_2C_2O_4$, is oxidised to carbon dioxide by potassium manganate(VII), $KMnO_4$, in acidic solution according to the equation

$$2KMnO_4 + 3H_2SO_4 + 5H_2C_2O_4 \rightarrow 2MnSO_4 + 10CO_2 + K_2SO_4 + 8H_2O$$

Hence:
$$\frac{\text{moles KMnO}_4}{\text{moles H}_2\text{C}_2\text{O}_4} = \frac{2}{5}$$

∴
$$\frac{\text{molarity} \times \text{volume (in dm}^3\text{) of KMnO}_4}{\text{molarity} \times \text{volume (in dm}^3\text{) of H}_2\text{C}_2\text{O}_4} = \frac{2}{5}$$

It was found that 25.0 cm^3 of 0.05 M ethanedioic acid solution was oxidised by 26.7 cm^3 of potassium manganate(VII) solution of unknown molarity.

Hence:
$$\frac{\text{M(KMnO}_4\text{)} \times 0.0267}{0.05 \times 0.025} = \frac{2}{5}$$

Calculate the molarity of the potassium manganate(VII) solution.

Question 11   Calculate the volume (in cm^3) of 0.01 M silver nitrate solution which would be required to react with a solution made by dissolving 2.05×10^{-4} moles of sodium chloride in water.   The equation is

$$AgNO_3(aq) \; + \; NaCl(aq) \; \rightarrow \; AgCl(s) \; + \; NaNO_3(aq)$$

Hence:
$$\frac{\text{moles AgNO}_3}{\text{moles NaCl}} \; = \; \frac{1}{1}$$

∴
$$\frac{\text{molarity} \times \text{volume (in dm}^3) \text{ of AgNO}_3}{\text{moles NaCl}} \; = \; \frac{1}{1}$$

Note 2.05×10^{-4} is 0.000205 written in *standard form* for convenience.   To enter this in your calculator, press 2.05, then *exp*, then +/- and finally 4.

Answers to questions in this chapter
1. 8.52 mol   2. 3 mol   3. 300 mol   4. 1.25 mol   5. 25 mol   6. 1.9 mol KMnO$_4$, 7.6 mol H$_2$SO$_4$ & 9.5 mol FeSO$_4$ 7. 0.0911 M   8. 0.120 M   9. 4500 mol   10. 0.0187 M   11. 20.5 cm^3

Chapter 5

MOLES OF GASES

From the standpoint of chemistry there is nothing special about a gas. Covalent bonds are seldom broken when a substance becomes a gas; a molecule of water, for instance, is always the same, regardless of whether the water exists as solid, liquid or gas. The chemical properties of a substance are therefore independent of its state. What *is* special about a gas is that, in general terms, mass is low and volume is high; consequently, it is very difficult to weigh a gas accurately. It is much more convenient to record the volume of a gas rather than its mass - which raises the interesting question, "How do we convert the volume of a gas to an amount in moles?"

Many years ago a scientist called Avogadro suggested that *equal volumes of all gases, under the same conditions of temperature and pressure, contain equal numbers of molecules.* He had no way of proving this statement, which became known as *Avogadro's hypothesis* (later, *Avogadro's law.*) Effectively, one molecule of any gas (under identical conditions) occupies a constant volume. Since there is a fixed number of molecules in a mole, it follows that **one mole of any gas, under similar conditions, occupies a constant volume. By experiment, this volume is approximately 22.4 dm^3 at standard temperature and pressure (s.t.p.),** i.e. a temperature of 273 K and a pressure of 101 325 Nm^{-2} ($\approx$ 24 dm^3 at 293 K, i.e. 20 $^{\circ}$C).

Notes

1   "Standard temperature" in the context of gases is different from the standard temperature (298 K) used in other areas of chemistry, e.g. energetics.

2   Various pressure units are in use at the present time. The SI unit is the newton per square metre, Nm^{-2}, often referred to as the pascal, Pa. Unfortunately, this is a very small unit and, for convenience, chemists usually adopt the kilopascal, kPa, which is 1000 Pa.

A non-SI unit of pressure, the *atmosphere* (atm) is still widely used for purposes of day-to-day chemistry. 1 atm = 101 325 Nm^{-2} $\approx$ 100 000 Nm^{-2}.

Recently, the inconvenience of the Nm^{-2} as a pressure unit is being overcome by the use of the *bar*, which is 100 000 Nm^{-2}. Hence, 1 atm = 101 325 Nm^{-2} = 1.013 bar.

The *millibar* (mbar), which is a thousandth of a bar, is also in use.
1 atm = 1.013 bar = 1013 mbar.

All of this is terribly confusing for you, the poor student. Whatever are you to do? Give up chemistry and try something easier, like sociology? *No!* The answer is to stick to the pressure units adopted by the examiner when he/she set the question. Except when carrying out calculations on the general gas equation (see below), you are seldom justified in converting pressure units.

"Volume to moles" calculations are very common throughout 'A' level chemistry.

Example How many moles of oxygen are represented by 500 cm^3 of O_2 (g) at s.t.p.?

If 22.4 dm^3 O_2 = 1 mol,
then 1 dm^3 O_2 = 1/22.4 mol,
and 500 cm^3 O_2 = 0.5 dm^3 O_2 = 1/22.4 × 0.5 = 0.0223 mol

In general: **MOLES = VOLUME IN DM^3** / **22.4**

Similar logic will take us back from moles to a volume.

Example What volume at s.t.p. would be occupied by 0.05 mol of carbon dioxide?

1 mol CO_2 occupies 22.4 dm^3 at s.t.p.
∴ 0.05 mol CO_2 occupies 22.4 × 0.05 = 1.12 dm^3

Questions

1 Calculate the amount in moles of each gas in the following. (All volumes relate to s.t.p.)
a) 10 cm^3 of hydrogen
b) 1 dm^3 of nitrogen
c) 1 m^3 of chlorine (*Hint* 1 m^3 = 1000 dm^3)

2 Calculate the volume at s.t.p. which would be occupied by each of the following.
a) 0.1 mol of methane
b) 100 mol of helium

You will appreciate that few laboratories are as cold as 273 K (i.e. 0 °C) even when schools and colleges are on a vast economy run in the winter months! The question therefore arises, "If the volume of a gas is measured under non-standard conditions, how many moles are present?"

To answer this, we use what is known as the *general gas equation*. Derived from three laws of physics, namely Boyle's law, Charles' law and the Law of pressures, in its simplest form it reads:

$$pV = nRT$$

where p is the pressure in Nm^{-2},
  V is the volume in m^3,
  n is the amount of gas in mol,
  R is the gas constant, 8.31 JK^{-1} mol^{-1},
and T is the temperature in kelvins.

All calculations on the general gas equation must be carried out in these pure SI units.

Not all examining boards require these calculations. Check your syllabus and, if you are free to do so, cut the rest of this section and move on to 'Reactions involving gases' on p. 25.

Example What volume, at 20 °C and a pressure of 0.96 atm, would be occupied by 1.5 mol of nitrogen?

$$V = \frac{nRT}{p}$$

n = 1.5 mol
T = 273 + 20 = 293 K
p (pressure in SI units) is not so obvious.
If 1 atm = 101 325 Nm^{-2},

then   0.96 atm = 101 325 × 0.96 = 97 272 Nm^{-2}

∴ $$V = \frac{1.5 \times 8.31 \times 293}{97\,272} = 0.0375\ m^3 = 37.5\ dm^3$$

Example What would be the mass of hydrogen occupying a volume of 750 cm^3 at 15 °C and a pressure of 99 kPa?

Since $n = m/Mr$ (where m = mass in grams), the general gas equation may be rewritten

$$pV = \frac{mRT}{M_r}$$

or $$m = \frac{pVM_r}{RT}$$

Again, the value for p in Nm^{-2} must be worked out before we can tackle the main calculation.

1 kPa = 1000 Pa = 1000 Nm^{-2}
∴   99 kPa = 99 × 10^3 Nm^{-2}

V = 0.75 dm^3 = 0.75 × 10^{-3} m^3
M_r = 2   (*Note* Hydrogen is diatomic; the formula is H_2.)
T = 273 + 15 = 288 K

∴ $$m = \frac{99 \times 10^3 \times 0.75 \times 10^{-3} \times 2}{8.31 \times 288}$$

= 0.0620 g

Sometimes, in examinations, you are given the pressure, volume and temperature of a mass of gas, and asked to calculate its M_r. See if you can do this one.

Question 3 1.47 g of an acid gas occupied a volume of 1 dm^3 at a temperature of 298 K and a pressure of 1 bar. Calculate its relative molecular mass. (1 bar = 100 000 Nm^{-2}; 1 dm^3 = 10^{-3} m^3)

Reactions Involving Gases

Avogadro's law tells you that the volumes of gases (measured under the same conditions) are related to the numbers of molecules they contain. It follows that, in a gas reaction, **the volume ratio in which the gases react** (as measured in the laboratory) **is the same as the molecular ratio** (as shown by the equation). This in turn is the same as the mole ratio.

This important principle should be borne in mind whenever you are carrying out calculations on gas reactions. You will find it applied in several places in this book; meanwhile, to give you confidence, let's apply the principle to the following question.

Example Hydrogen sulphide burns in oxygen to give sulphur dioxide and water:

$$2H_2S(g) \; + \; 3O_2(g) \; \rightarrow \; 2SO_2(g) \; + \; 2H_2O(g)$$

If 4 dm^3 of hydrogen sulphide were allowed to burn in 10 dm^3 of oxygen at a pressure of 1 atm, what would be the final volume of the gaseous mixture if it were measured at 383 K?

The first thing you must do, in questions of this sort, is to focus on the conditions, especially the temperature, to decide whether H_2O is formed as liquid water (which has a negligible volume) or water vapour - having a significant volume which must be included in the calculation. Here, the temperature is 383 K (110 °C), which is above the boiling point of water. Consequently, there is water *vapour* in the final mixture and you must take this into account.

$$2H_2S(g) \; + \; 3O_2(g) \; \rightarrow \; 2SO_2(g) \; + \; 2H_2O(g)$$

Molecules reacting	2	+ 3	→ 2	+ 2	
∴ volumes reacting	2 dm^3	+ 3 dm^3	→ 2 dm^3	+ 2 dm^3	
× 2	4 dm^3	+ 6 dm^3	→ 4 dm^3	+ 4 dm^3	

It is tempting to argue that the final volume is 8 dm^3, comprising 4 dm^3 SO$_2$ + 4 dm^3 H$_2$O. However, look more closely and you will see that not all the oxygen supplied at the start (10 dm^3) is being used up; only 6 dm^3. 4 dm^3 of O$_2$ is said to be *in excess*. (This is to ensure complete combustion of the H$_2$S.) The final volume, therefore, is 12 dm^3, i.e. 4 dm^3 SO$_2$(g) + 4 dm^3 H$_2$O + 4 dm^3 excess O$_2$.

Now try a related calculation for yourself.

Question 4   What is the minimum volume of *air* required for the complete combustion of 500 cm^3 of methane? (Assume that all gas volumes are measured under the same conditions.)
Hints   Write the equation, look at the molecular ratio, calculate the volume of O$_2$ and *then* the volume of air, assuming that air contains 20% by volume of O$_2$.

Answers to questions in this chapter

1. a) 4.46 × 10^{-4} b) 0.0446   c) 44.6   2. a) 2.24 dm^3 b) 2240 dm^3 3. 36.4   4. 5 dm^3

Chapter 6

✤ EMPIRICAL FORMULAE

Ask the question, "What is empirical formula?", and you will get different answers from different people. Students usually say it is the "simplest formula", whereas those who know the true meaning of the word *empirical* will tell you it is a "formula found by experiment". All of which is true, but misses the real point, which is that the **empirical formula of a compound shows the mole ratio of atoms of each element,** in simple whole numbers.

In itself, the empirical formula of a compound is of little value. Essentially, it is a stepping-stone on the way to the molecular formula and the structural formula. As such, however, it is so important that simple empirical formula calculations usually feature at GCSE. In such questions the examiner tells you *percentage composition,* i.e. the percentages (by mass) of each element present in the compound. Your job is to turn the *mass ratio* of atoms into a *mole ratio* by dividing by their respective relative atomic masses. (Remember that, for the atomic form of elements, we always convert grams to moles by dividing by A_r.) The result will be the correct mole ratio, but generally not in simple whole numbers. To achieve this we divide by the smallest and then, if we still do not have whole numbers, we multiply by a low integer, usually 2 or 3.

Example Sodium thiosulphate contains 29.1% of sodium, 40.5% of sulphur and 30.4% of oxygen. What is its empirical formula?

	Na	S	O
Percentage by mass	29.1	40.5	30.4
Divide by A_r	$\dfrac{29.1}{23}$	$\dfrac{40.5}{32}$	$\dfrac{30.4}{16}$
	= 1.27	= 1.27	= 1.90

As always, you must work to three significant figures. **Do not approximate at this stage.**

Divide by 1.27*	1	1	1.496 ≈ 1.5
Multiply by 2	2	2	3

i.e. the empirical formula is $Na_2S_2O_3$.

* You may approximate at this stage but only to a limited extent, e.g. 1.496 ≈ 1.5. You are *not* justified in turning 1.496 into 1!

Although this type of calculation is by no means unknown at 'A' level, you will find that many are less straightforward. Very often you will have the additional task of working out the percentage composition from analytical data before carrying out the type of calculation shown above.

Example 1.50 g of an organic compound containing only carbon, hydrogen and oxygen gave, on complete combustion, 3.41 g of carbon dioxide and 1.40 g of water. Calculate its empirical formula.

Percentage of carbon

3.41 g CO_2 is 3.41 ÷ 44 = 0.0775 mol CO_2 (44 is the M_r of CO_2)
1 mol CO_2 contains 1 mol C,

∴ we have 0.0775 mol C, of mass 0.0775 × 12 = 0.93 g C.

(The remainder of the 3.41 g of CO_2 is accounted for by combined oxygen.)

∴ percentage carbon = $\dfrac{\text{mass of carbon}}{\text{mass of compound}}$ × 100 = $\dfrac{0.93}{1.50}$ × 100 = 62.0%

Percentage of hydrogen

1.40 g H_2O is 1.40 ÷ 18 = 0.0778 mol H_2O

1 mol H_2O contains 2 mol H,

∴   we have 0.0778 × 2 = 0.156 mol H, of mass 0.156 × 1 = 0.156 g H.

∴   percentage hydrogen = $\dfrac{\text{mass of hydrogen}}{\text{mass of compound}}$ × 100 = $\dfrac{0.156}{1.50}$ × 100 = 10.4%

Percentage of oxygen

Oxygen content is difficult to estimate directly and is usually obtained by difference.
62.0 + 10.4 = 72.4   100 - 72.4 = 27.6 % of oxygen

Now we can do the earlier type of calculation.

	C	H	O
Percentage by mass	62.0	10.4	27.6
Divide by A_r	$\dfrac{62.0}{12}$	$\dfrac{10.4}{1}$	$\dfrac{27.6}{16}$
	= 5.17	= 10.4	= 1.73
Divide by 1.73	2.99	6.01	1

i.e. the empirical formula is C_3H_6O.

To determine the percentage of a halogen (i.e. chlorine, bromine or iodine) in a halide, it is customary to convert the halogen into a silver halide by means of excess silver nitrate. (If the compound is covalent, halide ions have first to be formed from halogen atoms. This may be done by oxidation with nitric acid, or perhaps by reaction with sodium hydroxide.) The calculation is then performed as above.

Example   0.75 g of an organic compound, on complete combustion, yielded 0.653 g of carbon dioxide and 0.401 g of water. 0.68 g of the same compound, on treatment with nitric acid and silver nitrate, gave 1.93 g of silver chloride. Calculate the empirical formula.

Calculations identical with those above show that the carbon content is 23.7% and the hydrogen content is 5.95%. *Please check these figures and make sure that you agree with them.* By similar reasoning we can get the chlorine content. The M_r of AgCl is 143.5,

∴   1.93 g AgCl is 1.93 ÷ 143.5 = 0.0134 mol AgCl.
       1 mol AgCl contains 1 mol Cl,

∴   we have 0.0134 mol Cl ≡ 0.0134 × 35.5 = 0.0477 g Cl.

∴   percentage chlorine = $\dfrac{\text{mass of chlorine}}{\text{mass of compound}}$ × 100 = $\dfrac{0.477}{0.68}$ × 100 = 70.2%

The total of these percentages = 23.7 + 5.95 + 70.2 = 99.9 %, telling us that there is no combined oxygen in this compound.

Now finish off this calculation in the usual way and see if you get the same answer as me! I make it CH_3Cl. If you disagree (or cannot do it) please ask your teacher.

Nitrogen compounds present a further complication in that nitrogen is usually estimated as ammonia.

Example An amide was found to contain 40.7 % of carbon and 8.47 % of hydrogen. On boiling 0.6 g of the compound with sodium hydroxide solution, the ammonia released was sufficient to neutralise 20.3 cm^3 of 0.5 M hydrochloric acid. Calculate the empirical formula.

Amides (compounds of general formula RCONH$_2$) react with aqueous sodium hydroxide to give the sodium salt of a carboxylic acid and ammonia:

$$RCONH_2 \ + \ NaOH \ \rightarrow \ RCOONa \ + \ NH_3$$

The amount of ammonia given off is found from the amount of hydrochloric acid which it neutralises:

$$NH_3(g) \ + \ HCl(aq) \rightarrow \ NH_4Cl(aq)$$

Amount of HCl $=$ molarity $\times$ volume (in dm^3) $= \ 0.5 \times 0.0203 \ = \ 0.0102$ mol

Because of the 1:1 mole ratio in which NH$_3$ and HCl react together, the amount of NH$_3$ is also 0.0102 mol.

The equation at the top shows that every atom of combined nitrogen in the amide produces one molecule of ammonia,
∴   number of moles of N atoms $=$ number of moles of NH$_3$ molecules $= \ 0.0102$,
∴   mass of N atoms $= \ 0.0102 \times 14 \ = \ 0.143$ g

∴   percentage nitrogen $= \dfrac{\text{mass of nitrogen}}{\text{mass of compound}} \times \ 100 \ = \dfrac{0.143}{0.6} \times 100 \ = \ 23.8\%$

Again, it would be sensible if you were to finish this question by yourself. The answer should be C$_2$H$_5$NO; see what you make it!

Before we have a look at a more demanding type of empirical formula calculation, how about practising the sorts we have done so far?

Questions
1   Table salt is not pure sodium chloride; it also contains some magnesium carbonate. When 0.509 g of a sample of table salt was dissolved in dilute nitric acid and treated with excess silver nitrate solution, the resulting precipitate of silver chloride weighed 1.17 g. Calculate the percentage (by mass) of chloride ions in the salt. A_r: Cl = 35.5; Ag = 108.
Hint The dilute nitric acid does not feature in the calculation. Its role is to dissolve the magnesium carbonate, to give magnesium nitrate in solution. The latter does not react with silver nitrate.
2   In determining the bromine content of an unknown bromoalkane, 1.48 g of the compound was first boiled under a reflux condenser with aqueous sodium hydroxide in order to produce bromide ions:

$$RBr(l) \ + \ NaOH(aq) \rightarrow \ ROH(aq) \ + \ Na^+Br^-(aq)$$

The solution was then acidified with dilute nitric acid and treated with excess silver nitrate solution. 2.03 g of silver bromide were precipitated. Calculate the percentage (by mass) of bromine in the bromoalkane. A_r: Br = 80; Ag = 108.

When calculating empirical formula it is not always essential or, indeed, desirable to proceed via percentage composition. The examiner may tell you or expect you to find the amount in moles of each sort of atom (i.e. of each element in the compound) and then work out a simple whole number ratio by dividing by the smallest in the usual way.

Example Nitrogen and chlorine form an unstable chloride, 12.05 g of which contain 10.65 g of chlorine. Calculate the number of moles of each element in 12.05 g of the compound, and hence its empirical formula. A_r: N = 14; Cl = 35.5.

Mass of nitrogen = 12.05 - 10.65 = 1.40 g

		N		Cl
Masses/grams		1.40		10.65
∴ moles		$\dfrac{1.40}{14}$		$\dfrac{10.65}{35.5}$
	=	0.1	=	0.3
Divide by the smallest		1		3

i.e. the empirical formula is NCl_3.

Here is a harder one, which I will lead you through.

Question 3 A compound X contains carbon, hydrogen and nitrogen only. On combustion, 0.2 g of the compound gave 0.568 g of carbon dioxide and 0.135 g of water. A further 0.2 g of X was then oxidised with concentrated sulphuric acid so that combined nitrogen was converted into ammonium sulphate, which, on boiling with excess aqueous sodium hydroxide, released gaseous ammonia equivalent to 21.5 cm^3 of 0.100 M hydrochloric acid. Calculate the number of moles of each element in 0.2 g of compound X and hence the empirical formula of the compound.

First find the number of moles of CO_2 and hence the number of moles of C; also the number of moles of H_2O and hence moles of H. Then calculate the number of moles of HCl used in the titration; hence the number of moles of NH_3 and the number of moles of N.

Once you have got the number of moles of C, H and N, all you have to do is divide by the smallest to get a simple whole number ratio.

Here is another question, which again I'll lead you through. It is as difficult as anything you are likely to meet, so if you can do this you really are on top of the subject!

Question 4 The Group 3 element indium forms a chloride, 0.0372 g of which dissociated on dissolving in water to release chloride ions which were titrated by 16.0 cm^3 of 0.025 M aqueous silver nitrate. Calculate the empirical formula of the indium chloride. A_r: Cl = 35.5; In = 115.

Wherever do we start? There is only one place we *can* start, and that is with the experimental data. We are told that, in a titration, 16.0 cm^3 of 0.025 M $AgNO_3$(aq) are used. What can we work out from this? Only one thing - moles of AgNO $_3$. Do it! (I make it 4×10^{-4} mol.)

Each mole of silver nitrate gives a mole of silver ions in solution:

$$AgNO_3(aq) \rightarrow Ag^+(aq) + NO_3^-(aq)$$

∴   we have 4×10^{-4} mol of silver ions.

These silver ions react with chloride ions from the indium chloride in a 1:1 ratio:

$$Ag^+(aq) \; + \; Cl^-(aq) \; \rightarrow \; AgCl(s)$$

∴   we have 4×10^{-4} mol of chloride ions.

If we can get the number of moles of indium, we can easily find the In:Cl mole ratio. But how? Think! We know the mass of the compound (0.0372 g) and we can easily find the mass of Cl (by multiplying the number of moles by 35.5). Subtracting one from the other will give the mass of In, from which we can get moles of In. Finally, work out the mole ratio.

For compounds containing covalent ions (e.g. SO_4^{2-}, CO_3^{2-}, NH_4^+), the empirical formula is always obtained from the mole ratio of the ions. You will not be given the percentage composition.

Example   1.50 g of anhydrous sodium sulphate, on treatment with dilute hydrochloric acid and excess aqueous barium chloride, gave a precipitate of barium sulphate which, after being filtered off, dried and weighed, was found to have a mass of 2.46 g. Calculate the empirical formula of sodium sulphate.

A_r: O = 16; Na = 23; S = 32; Ba = 137.

The equation for the precipitation reaction is:

$$Ba^{2+}(aq) \; + \; SO_4^{2-}(aq) \rightarrow \; BaSO_4(s)$$

Hence the number of moles of sulphate ions = number of moles of barium sulphate. Try it! (I make it 0.0106 mol.)

Knowing that the relative ionic mass of SO_4^{2-} = 32 + 64 = 96, you can calculate the mass of SO_4^{2-}. (1.02 g, I think.)

Hence the mass of Na^+ ions = 1.50 - 1.02 = 0.48 g

Finally, find the number of moles of Na^+ ions and hence the mole ratio. Your answer should be Na_2SO_4.

To conclude, here is an interesting question involving a compound with *two* covalent ions!

Question 5   0.100 g of ammonium carbonate, when treated with excess dilute hydrochloric acid, produced 23.3 cm^3 (at s.t.p.) of carbon dioxide. A further 0.100 g of the same compound, on boiling with excess aqueous sodium hydroxide, liberated ammonia which was found to neutralise 20.4 cm^3 of 0.102 M hydrochloric acid. Calculate the number of moles of CO_3^{2-} ions and NH_4^+ ions in 0.100 g of ammonium carbonate, and hence the empirical formula of this compound.
      1 mol of gas at s.t.p. occupies 22.4 dm^3.

Hint Ionic equations for the reactions are as follows:

$$CO_3^{2-} \; + \; 2H^+ \; \rightarrow \; CO_2 \; + \; H_2O$$
$$NH_4^+ \; + \; OH^- \; \rightarrow \; NH_3 \; + \; H_2O$$

Answers to questions in this chapter
1. 56.9%   2. 58.4%   3. C_6H_7N 4. $InCl_2$ 5. $(NH_4)_2CO_3$

Chapter 7

MOLECULAR FORMULAE

The *molecular formula* of a covalent compound shows the numbers of atoms of each element which are chemically bonded together in one molecule of that compound. It may be identical with its empirical formula or may be a multiple of it. For example, for methane, the empirical formula and the molecular formula are both CH_4, but for ethane the empirical formula is CH_3 while the molecular formula is C_2H_6.

Do not confuse molecular formula with *structural formula*, which literally shows the structure of the molecule, i.e. the way in which the atoms are bonded together. For ethane, the structural formula is as follows:

$$\begin{array}{cc} H & H \\ | & | \\ H-C- & C-H \\ | & | \\ H & H \end{array}$$

This may be abbreviated to CH_3CH_3. (The full structural formula may also be referred to as a *displayed formula.*)

An ionic compound cannot have a molecular formula. In such cases the "formula" is an empirical formula in that it represents the ratio of the ions, e.g. for barium chloride, the formula $BaCl_2$ shows that Ba^{2+} and Cl^- ions are present in a 1:2 ratio. However, in examinations you are often asked to "calculate the formula" of an ionic compound or one of unknown bonding and such calculations are included here.

Molecular formulae calculations are a development of empirical formulae calculations and are easy **provided you can cope with the latter**; so do make sure you are on top of *Chapter 6* before tackling this one. There are two basic types of calculations.

i.   Those in which the empirical formula is first worked out, as described in *Chapter 6*. Information on relative molecular mass, either provided by the examiner or worked out by you in a subsidiary calculation, is then used to find the number of times the molecular formula is greater than the empirical formula.

ii.   Those in which data are provided on the preparation of a compound; or else on its decomposition, combustion or other reaction. Such calculations are very similar to many of those for empirical formulae, the only difference being that additional information may be given so that you can be sure you are calculating the molecular formula of a compound and not its empirical formula.

Molecular Formula From Empirical Formula And Relative Molecular Mass

In the simplest possible type of calculation the M_r is given to you.

Example   An organic bromide contains, by mass, 22.2% carbon, 3.70% hydrogen and 74.5% bromine. Given that its relative molecular mass is 216, calculate its molecular formula.
A_r: H = 1; C = 12; Br = 80.

The first task is to calculate the empirical formula, as described above. Please do it! (It should work out to be C_2H_4Br.)

The relative empirical formula mass is therefore $24 + 4 + 80 = 108$. If we divide the relative molecular mass of 216 by this value we get a factor of 2, telling us that the molecular formula must be twice the empirical formula, i.e. $C_4H_8Br_2$.

In more complicated calculations *you* have to find the M_r as well as the empirical formula. For gases we use the general gas equation, as described in *Chapter 5*. In other cases the results of a titration may be quoted.

Example   The empirical formula of a diprotic acid is CHO_2. 0.125 g of the acid was neutralised by 28.1 cm^3 of 0.099 M aqueous sodium hydroxide. Calculate the molecular formula of the acid.
A_r: H = 1;   C = 12;   O = 16.

We are told that the acid is diprotic; an older term is "dibasic". Essentially, this means that one molecule of the acid has *two* hydrogen atoms which can be replaced by metal atoms in neutralisation reactions. (The term *diprotic* literally means that one molecule of the acid can release two protons, H^+.) Reaction between the acid and sodium hydroxide therefore occurs in a 1:2 mole ratio. In general terms, where 'A' represents an anion, we can write an equation:

$$H_2A \ + \ 2NaOH \ \rightarrow \ Na_2A \ + \ 2H_2O$$

Bearing in mind that, for a substance in solution, moles = molarity $\times$ volume (in dm^3),
moles of NaOH = 0.099×0.0281 = 2.78×10^{-3}
∴   moles of acid   = $(2.78 \times 10^{-3}) \div 2$ = 1.39×10^{-3}

If 1.39×10^{-3} mol of the acid has a mass of 0.125 g then, dividing by 1.39×10^{-3},

1 mol of the acid has a mass of $0.125 \div (1.39 \times 10^{-3})$ = $89.9 \approx 90$,
i.e. the molar mass is 90 g, from which it follows that the M_r is 90.

Now see if you can finish off this question. Remember that we already have the empirical formula, CHO_2, so you should have no difficulty in showing that the molecular formula is $C_2H_2O_4$.

Molecular Formula From The Preparation Of A Compound

Example   2.14 g of a Group 1 metal oxide (general formula M_2O) are made by burning 1.00 g of a metal (M) in oxygen. Identify the metal and hence write the formula of the oxide. A_r: O = 16

This is similar to an empirical formula type of calculation in which you have to find the number of moles of each type of atom.

Mass of O atoms   = $2.14 - 1.00$ = 1.14 g
∴   moles of O atoms   = $1.14 \div 16$ = 0.0713

Because you are told that the oxide is of general formula M_2O, you can argue that moles of M atoms = 0.0713×2 = 0.143. This, as the examiner tells you, has a mass of 1.00 g.

Bearing in mind that, for the atomic form of an element, moles = mass $\div A_r$,
0.143   = $1.00 \div A_r$
∴ A_r = $1.00 \div 0.143$ = $6.99 \approx 7$

The Periodic Table tells you that the metal is lithium, so the formula of the oxide is Li_2O.

Question 1   Titanium is extracted from ilmenite, an ore which is essentially a mixed oxide of iron and titanium, formula $FeTiO_x$. Given that this substance contains 31.6% by mass of titanium, calculate the value of x. A_r: $O = 16$; $Ti = 48$; $Fe = 56$.
Hints   Aim at calculating the number of moles of Fe, Ti and O atoms in 100 g of ilmenite. Start with titanium: $31.6 \div 48 = 0.658$ mol Ti. Then, using the formula, write down number of moles of Fe. Next, work out the mass of oxygen (in 100 g ilmenite) and hence moles of O atoms. Finally find the mole ratio.

In a variation of this type of question, you are given information on a second product, i.e. a by-product of the reaction in which the main compound is formed.

Example   Vanadium can form three chlorides, VCl_2, VCl_3 and VCl_4. Which of these was formed when 5.10 g of the metal were dissolved in hydrochloric acid, releasing 3.36 dm^3 of hydrogen, measured at s.t.p.?   (1 mol of any gas at s.t.p. occupies a volume of 22.4 dm^3.) A_r: $V = 51$

If 22.4 dm^3 of hydrogen (at s.t.p.) is the volume of 1 mol H_2,
then   1 dm^3 is the volume of $1 \div 22.4$ $= 0.0446$ mol H_2,
and   3.36 dm^3 is the volume of $0.0446 \times 3.36 = 0.15$ mol H_2.

Because the formation of one molecule of H_2 needs *two* molecules of HCl, we can argue that the number of moles of HCl is $2 \times 0.15 = 0.3$. Hence there is 0.3 mol Cl atoms.

How much vanadium are we starting with?
5.1 g V $= 5.1 \div 51$ $= 0.1$ mol V.

∴   moles of V:moles of Cl $= 0.1:0.3$,
i.e.   the mole ratio is 1:3 and the formula of the compound is VCl_3.

In the following question, you are asked to find the formula of a chloride from information on the mass of chlorine produced when it is formed by the decomposition of a higher chloride (i.e. one with a higher chlorine content).

Example   Lead forms two chlorides; one is a yellow oil (A) and the other a white solid (B). Calculate the formula of each, given the following information.
i.   The oil (A) contains 59.6% of lead.
ii.   Thermal decomposition of 2.59 g of the oil (A) produces 2.06 g of the solid (B) and 0.530 g of chlorine.
A_r: $Cl = 35.5$; $Pb = 207$.

You can find the empirical formula of the yellow oil (A) in the usual way.

	Pb	Cl
Percentages of atoms by mass	59.6	40.4
Moles of atoms	$59.6 \div 207$	$40.4 \div 35.5$
	$= 0.288$	$= 1.14$
∴ mole ratio of atoms	$0.288 \div 0.288$	$1.14 \div 0.288$
	$= 1$	$= 4$

i.e. the empirical formula is $PbCl_4$. In the absence of further information, you must leave the calculation here.

To find the formula of the lower lead chloride (B), you must focus on the chlorine which is lost when 2.59 g of the oil (A) is heated. In this way you can find, first, the masses of lead atoms and chlorine atoms, then the number of moles, and finally the mole ratio.

The mass of lead remains exactly as it was,

i.e.	mass of Pb in 2.59 g of the oil (A)		= $2.59 \times 59.6/100$ = 1.54 g
$\therefore$	mass of Pb in the white solid (B)		= 1.54 g
$\therefore$	mass of Cl in B	= 2.06 - 1.54	= 0.520 g
$\therefore$	moles of Pb	= 1.54 ÷ 207	= 7.44×10^{-3}
and	moles of Cl	= 0.520 ÷ 35.5	= 1.46×10^{-2}

Finally, dividing by the smaller (7.44×10^{-3}) shows you that the mole ratio of Pb:Cl = 1:2, i.e. the formula is $PbCl_2$.

Molecular Formula From The Decomposition Of A Compound

Learn by doing !

Example 10 cm^3 of a gaseous metal hydride decomposes on warming into the metal (M) and 20 cm^3 of hydrogen. (Both gas volumes relate to room temperature and pressure.) What is the formula of the hydride?

Any substance whose name ends in '-ide' is a *binary compound*, i.e. one which is derived from two elements only; so a *hydride* contains hydrogen and one other element. The formula could be written MH_n; our job is to calculate the value of n.

We have already seen that the volume ratio in which gases react (as measured in the laboratory) is the same as the molecular ratio. Here,

	MH_n	$\rightarrow$	H_2		
Volume ratio	10		20		
$\therefore$ molecular ratio	10		20	=	1:2

i.e. one molecule of the hydride gives two molecules of H_2, from four *atoms* of hydrogen.

$\therefore$ one molecule of the hydride must contain four atoms of hydrogen, i.e. the formula is MH_4.

Molecular Formula From The Combustion Of A Compound

Although a few inorganic compounds are combustible, we are generally concerned in this context with organic ones. Excess oxygen is used to ensure complete combustion, so that combined carbon is converted to carbon dioxide (rather than carbon monoxide) and combined hydrogen is converted to water. The number of molecules of oxygen consumed by one molecule of the organic compound, and the number of molecules of carbon dioxide which are formed, vary from one organic compound to another, e.g

	$CH_4(g)$	+	$2O_2(g)$	$\rightarrow$	$CO_2(g)$	+	$2H_2O(l)$
No. of molecules	1		2		1		

	$C_2H_6(g)$	+	$3.5O_2(g)$	$\rightarrow$	$2CO_2(g)$	+	$3H_2O(l)$
No. of molecules	1		3.5		2		

	$C_2H_4(g)$	+	$3O_2(g)$	$\rightarrow$	$2CO_2(g)$	+	$2H_2O(l)$
No. of molecules	1		3		2		

34

These numbers of molecules depend on the molecular formula of the compound and could well provide a route to the molecular formula if they could be determined. Although the molecular ratio cannot be measured directly, the volume ratio can be found by experiment, and you will recall that (for any gas reaction) the volume ratio is equal to the molecular ratio.

The apparatus which is used for measuring gas volumes is called a *eudiometer*. It consists essentially of a robust, graduated glass tube into which are sealed two platinum electrodes. A spark can be passed between them to create a controlled explosion, during which the organic compound undergoes complete combustion.

The experimenter knows the volume of gas introduced (i.e. the compound under test) and also the volume of oxygen. After explosion, the eudiometer contains $CO_2(g)$ and excess $O_2(g)$: the volume of this mixture is recorded. **Since the apparatus is now at room temperature, water will be produced as liquid water, of negligible volume.** The question now is, "How much of this mixture is CO_2 and how much is unreacted O_2?" To resolve this, the gas is allowed to stand over aqueous alkali, usually potassium hydroxide, which absorbs the carbon dioxide:

$$2KOH(aq) \ + \ CO_2(g) \ \rightarrow \ K_2CO_3(aq) \ + \ H_2O(l)$$

The decrease in volume thus indicates how much CO_2 has been formed. The residual gas (i.e. which is not absorbed by the KOH) is excess O_2: subtracting this from the volume of O_2 which was taken at the start of the experiment gives the volume of O_2 used up on combustion.

Example 10 cm^3 of a gaseous hydrocarbon were sparked with 80 cm^3 (an excess) of oxygen. The 65 cm^3 of gas remaining after the explosion were reduced to 45 cm^3 on standing over an aqueous solution of potassium hydroxide. Calculate the molecular formula of the hydrocarbon.

Your first task, in questions of this kind, is to interpret the data. You must work out, by logic, the volume of O_2 which has been used up on combustion, and the volume of CO_2 which has been formed.

Focus on the volume of gas (45 cm^3) remaining at the end of the experiment. This is excess O_2 (i.e. unreacted O_2). Hence, the volume of O_2 used on combustion = 80 - 45 = 35 cm^3.

The 65 cm^3 of gas which is present immediately after the explosion is accounted for partly by CO_2 and partly by excess O_2. Since we know that the volume of excess O_2 is 45 cm^3, the volume of CO_2 must be 65 - 45 = 20 cm^3.

You must now write an equation for the combustion of the hydrocarbon. Obviously, you cannot write an ordinary chemical equation, because you do not know the identity of the compound, but you can write a *general* equation for any hydrocarbon, C_xH_y

$$C_xH_y(g) \ + \ (x + {}^y/_4)O_2(g) \ \rightarrow \ xCO_2(g) \ + \ {}^y/_2H_2O(l)$$

Many students memorise this equation but there is no need to do so. It is easy to balance as and when necessary, if you tackle C first, then H and finally O. (Put in x CO_2 to balance C atoms, then $^y/_2H_2O$ to balance H atoms, and finally $(x + {}^y/_4)O_2$ to balance O atoms.)

Now write in gas volumes:
        10 cm^3 35 cm^3 20 cm^3 Ignore $H_2O(l)$

To make this volume ratio match the molecular ratio shown in the equation, divide by 10:
$$1 \text{ cm}^3 \qquad 3.5 \text{ cm}^3 \qquad 2 \text{ cm}^3$$

Since, for the hydrocarbon, $1 = 1$, we can argue that, for O_2, $x + y/4 = 3.5$ and, for CO_2, $x = 2$. Substitution for $x = 2$ in the first of these mathematical equations gives

$$2 + \frac{y}{4} = 3.5$$
$$\therefore \qquad \frac{y}{4} = 3.5 - 2 = 1.5$$
$$\therefore \qquad y = 1.5 \times 4 = 6$$

i.e. the unknown hydrocarbon is C_2H_6.

Questions

2   When 5 cm^3 of a hydrocarbon were exploded with 30 cm^3 of oxygen, the residual volume was 22.5 cm^3, 15 cm^3 of which dissolved in KOH(aq). Calculate the molecular formula of the hydrocarbon.

3   1 volume of a gaseous alkane required 6.5 volumes of oxygen measured at the same temperature and pressure for complete combustion. What is the molecular formula of the alkane?

You may argue, with some justification, that exercises of this sort are fatuous. How often in real life are you likely to have the task of identifying a gaseous hydrocarbon? I have to admit that this type of calculation is somewhat old-fashioned and seldom appears on current examination papers, but I have noticed a development whereby a controlled combustion experiment is used to determine the number of carbon atoms in a molecule of *any* organic compound.

You may say that, if nothing is known about the compound, you cannot possibly write an equation - even a general one - for its combustion, and this is true. But if you represent the compound by a general formula C_nX, where n stands for the number of carbon atoms and X for the rest of the molecule, you can argue that one molecule of the compound gives rise to n molecules of carbon dioxide; hence 1 mol of the compound gives n mol of CO_2.

Example   An organic compound (A) is known to be either a mono- or dicarboxylic acid. Separate 0.001 mol samples of A are used in two experiments.
Experiment 1   Combustion produced 44.8 cm^3 CO_2, measured at s.t.p.
Experiment 2   Titration required 20.0 cm^3 of 0.100 M NaOH(aq).
Identify compound A. (Assume that 1 mol CO_2 occupies 22.4 dm^3 at s.t.p.)

This is a two-part calculation. First, you must use the data from *experiment 1* to work out the number of carbon atoms in one molecule of the compound. All you have to do is to find the number of moles of CO_2 produced by 0.001 mol of A, and then by 1 mol of A.

Since 22400 cm^3 is the volume of 1 mol CO_2,
then   1 cm^3 is the volume of $1 \div 22400 = 4.46 \times 10^{-5}$ mol CO_2,
and   44.8 cm^3 is the volume of $4.46 \times 10^{-5} \times 44.8 = 0.002$ mol CO_2.

$$1C_nX \rightarrow nCO_2$$
$$0.001 \text{mol} \rightarrow 0.002 \text{ mol}$$
$$\therefore \qquad 1 \text{ mol} \rightarrow 2 \text{ mol}$$

Thus, $n = 2$, i.e. A is a two carbon carboxylic acid.

Although this does not provide a firm identification of compound A, it does at least narrow the field to ethanoic acid, CH_3COOH, or ethanedioic acid, $(COOH)_2$. To decide which of these is correct, you must think how each of these acids would react with NaOH(aq). The former is a monoprotic acid, so 1 mol would need 1 mol of NaOH:

$$CH_3COOH \ + \ NaOH \ \rightarrow \ CH_3COONa \ + \ H_2O$$

But ethanedioic acid is diprotic (p. 32): 1 mol would need 2 mol of NaOH:

$$\begin{matrix} COOH \\ | \\ COOH \end{matrix} \quad + \ 2NaOH \ \rightarrow \begin{matrix} COONa \\ | \\ COONa \end{matrix} \quad + \ 2H_2O$$

The examiner tells you that 0.001 mol of A requires 20 cm³ of 0.100 M NaOH(aq).

Amount of NaOH = molarity × volume (in dm³) = 0.1 × 0.02 = 0.002 mol

If 0.001 mol of A needs 0.002 mol of NaOH, then 1 mol of A needs 2 mol of NaOH,
i.e.   compound A must be ethanedioic acid.

Here is another example, for you to try.

Question 3   When 250 cm³ of a volatile organic compound (measured at s.t.p.) were completely burnt, 0.0558 mol of carbon dioxide was obtained. How many carbon atoms are there in one molecule of the organic compound? (Assume that 1 mol CO_2 occupies 22.4 dm³ at s.t.p.)

Molecular Formula Of A Compound From Other Reactions

All sorts of reactions could, in principle, be used by imaginative examiners, and I cannot possibly discuss them all. However, I have noticed that quite frequently the unknown compound is a chloride, in which case its formula can be found by reaction with $AgNO_3$ - provided, of course, Cl is in the ionic form, Cl⁻ (see *Chapter 6.).*

Example   0.206 g of a liquid chloride of titanium was hydrolysed to give hydrochloric acid and a white solid. (The latter was filtered off and discarded.) Excess silver nitrate solution was added, precipitating 0.622 g of silver chloride. Calculate the formula of the titanium chloride.
A_r: Cl = 35.5;   Ti = 48;   Ag = 108.

It is a good rule to start calculations with the analytical results. Here, we are told that 0.622 g of AgCl was produced. Since the M_r of AgCl is 143.5, this is 0.622 ÷ 143.5 = 4.33×10^{-3} mol of AgCl.

The equation for the formation of silver chloride, $Ag^+(aq) \ + \ Cl^-(aq) \rightarrow \ AgCl(s)$, tells us that 1 mol Cl⁻ ions gives 1 mol AgCl,

∴	mol of chlorine	= 4.33×10^{-3}
∴	mass of chlorine	= $4.33 \times 10^{-3} \times 35.5$ = 0.154 g
∴	mass of titanium	= 0.206 - 0.154 = 0.0520 g
∴	mol of titanium	= 0.0520 ÷ 48 = 1.08×10^{-3}

i.e.   mole ratio of titanium : chlorine atoms = 1.08×10^{-3} : 4.33×10^{-3} = 1:4 (obtained by dividing by 1.08×10^{-3})

Hence the formula is $TiCl_4$.

Try this other example yourself.

Question 5   A solution of an unknown Group 2 metal chloride has a concentration of 104 g dm^{-3}. When 20.0 cm^3 of this solution were treated with excess silver nitrate solution, 2.87 g of silver chloride were produced. Calculate the relative atomic mass of the metal and hence identify the chloride.
A$_r$: Cl = 35.5; Ag = 108.
Hints   Because this is a Group 2 chloride, the general formula is MCl$_2$, so 1 mol MCl$_2$ produces 2 mol Cl$^-$ in solution. Thus, for 20.0 cm^3 of solution, you can find both the number of moles of MCl$_2$ and its mass. From these it is easy to calculate *M$_r$*.

Another empirical formula method that crops up in this context concerns nitrogen containing compounds which are persuaded to release ammonia on treatment with NaOH(aq). The ammonia is subsequently estimated by titration with a standard solution of an acid.

Question 6   On treatment with aqueous ammonia, copper(II) compounds form *ammines*, i.e. complexes of the kind [Cu(NH$_3$)$_n$]$^{2+}$ X^{2-}. Excess NaOH(aq) was added to 0.123 g of a copper(II) ammine of *M$_r$* 246 and the solution was boiled. The ammonia which was released was found to be chemically equivalent to 19.2 cm^3 of 0.104 M hydrochloric acid. How many moles of ammonia are chemically combined in one mole of the copper(II) ammine?

Hint   Work out moles of hydrochloric acid, and hence moles of ammonia released, remembering that they react together in a 1:1 mole ratio. Also work out moles of the copper(II) ammine. Then find how many moles of ammonia would be released by (and hence contained in) 1 mol of the complex.

Answers to questions in this chapter

1. 3   2. C$_3$H$_6$ 3. C$_4$H$_{10}$ 4. 5   5. BaCl$_2$ 6. 4

Chapter 8

USES OF FORMULAE

There are various mole calculations that do not fit neatly into any particular category, and I have decided to present them to you here because, in general, they utilise the formulae you have just been studying.

Some are essentially grams to moles calculations, achieved as usual by dividing mass by the M_r, or moles to grams, in which case you must multiply by M_r.

Example Analysis shows that the alcohol concentration in the blood of a motorist is 0.0205 M. Would the police be justified in prosecuting the motorist, given that the legal limit is 80 mg per 100 ml of blood? A_r: H = 1; C = 12; O = 16.

This is basically a moles to grams calculation.

Ethanol, C_2H_5OH, has an M_r of 46. We need to turn mol dm^{-3} into g dm^{-3} and then mg dm^{-3}.

$$\text{Concentration} = 0.0205 \times 46 = 0.943 \text{ g dm}^{-3}$$
$$= 0.943 \times 1000 = 943 \text{ mg dm}^{-3} \text{ (Because 1 g} = 1000 \text{ mg)}$$

We now need to carry out a second conversion, from mg dm^{-3} to mg per 100 ml. Bear in mind that 1 ml = 1 cm^3, and that 100 cm^3 = $^1/_{10}$ dm^3.

$\therefore$ concentration = $943 \div 10$ = 94.3 mg per 100 cm^3 = 94.3 mg per 100 ml. The motorist is therefore over the limit.

Others require you to look at the number of moles of atoms of a certain element contained in one mole of a compound.

Example Calculate the chlorine content of the cobalt complex, $CoCl_2(N_2H_4)_2$, made by treating a solution of cobalt(II) chloride with aqueous hydrazine, N_2H_4.
A_r: H = 1; N = 14; Cl = 35.5; Co = 59.

Because there are two moles of Cl atoms in one mole of the complex, the percentage of chlorine is represented by:

$$\frac{2Cl}{CoCl_2(N_2H_4)_2} \times 100 = \frac{71}{59 + 71 + 56 + 8} \times 100 = 36.6\%$$

Here is a more modern type of question for you to get your teeth into!

Question 1 Toothpaste for people with sensitive teeth may contain 10% by mass of strontium chloride hexahydrate, $SrCl_2.6H_2O$. Calculate the mass of a) strontium ions, and b) chloride ions, in a 3.00 g portion of toothpaste. A_r: H = 1; O = 16; Cl = 35.5; Sr = 88.

In some questions you are asked to proceed from the mass of an element to the mass of a compound which contains that element. This is essentially the opposite of a conversion (studied in *Chapter 6*) where you are given the mass of a compound and asked to calculate the mass of an element combined in it.

Example   Calculate the mass of tetraethyllead, $Pb(C_2H_5)_4$, that should be added to 1 dm^3 of petrol to provide a lead content of 0.1 g dm^{-3}. A_r: H = 1;   C = 12;   Pb = 207.

One mole of $Pb(C_2H_5)_4$ contains one mole of Pb atoms. The M_r of $Pb(C_2H_5)_4$ is 323,

∴   207 g Pb are provided by 323 g $Pb(C_2H_5)_4$,
∴   1 g Pb is provided by 323 ÷ 207   =   1.56 g $Pb(C_2H_5)_4$*,
∴   0.1 g Pb is provided by 1.56 × 0.1   =   0.156 g $Pb(C_2H_5)_4$.

* In questions of this kind it is unnecessary to work out the fraction at this stage. You'll find, with practice, that it saves time to carry the fraction over to the following line and just do one calculation at the end.

Once you feel confident about these simple proportion calculations you can take a short cut by using a *conversion factor*. The factor by which the 0.1 g of lead must be multiplied depends on the A_r of Pb (207) and the M_r of $Pb(C_2H_5)_4$ (323), so the answer is:

$$0.1 \times \frac{323}{207} = 0.156 \text{ g}$$

To those students who say, "I don't like this method because I always get my factor the wrong way up," I would reply, "Think! The mass of tetraethyllead must be greater than the mass of lead, because of all the carbon and hydrogen which you are also adding. Therefore, the conversion factor must be greater than 1. In other words, put the bigger figure at the top and the smaller one at the bottom:

CONVERSION FACTOR = $\dfrac{M_r \text{ (compound)}}{A_r \text{ (element)}}$

Question 2   It is recommended that the fluoride content of drinking water should be 1 part per million (i.e. 1 g F⁻ per 10^6 g H_2O). Calculate the mass of sodium fluoride which should be added to 1 tonne of water (i.e. 10^6 g of water) to provide this concentration of fluoride ions.
A_r: F = 19;   Na = 23.

Some questions hinge on the dissociation of compounds when they dissolve in water, i.e. their separation into ions. You will find that these are straightforward enough if you base your reasoning on the equations for dissociation.

Example   What is the molar concentration of hydrogen ions produced when 5 g of pure sulphuric acid are dissolved in 250 cm^3 of water ? (Neglect the volume change when the sulphuric acid is added to the water.) A_r: H = 1;   O = 16;   S = 32.

Dissociation is represented by the equation:

$$H_2SO_4(l) + aq \rightleftharpoons 2H^+(aq) + SO_4^{2-}(aq)$$

Sulphuric acid is a strong acid and we can assume that its dissociation is complete in dilute solution. (If dissociation were incomplete, we should have to take into account the fraction of the acid which dissociates. This aspect is covered in 'A' level texts in chapters on ionic equilibria.)

The M_r of H_2SO_4 is 98,

∴   we have $5 \div 98 = 0.0510$ mol H_2SO_4 in 250 cm^3 of solution.

Since 250 cm^3 = $^1/_4$ dm^3,
concentration of H_2SO_4 = $0.0510 \times 4 = 0.204$ mol dm^{-3}
The equation shows that 1 mol H_2SO_4 produces *2* mol H^+ ions,

∴   concentration of H^+ ions = $0.204 \times 2 = 0.408$ mol dm^{-3}

This question was quite easy because a kind-hearted examiner told you to neglect the volume change. This was justified because the volume increase (from 250 cm^3 to ~253 cm^3) was insignificant.

However, there are questions where the volume change *is* significant and cannot be ignored. You must realise that **when two solutions are mixed together each dilutes the other, so that each solution is less concentrated after mixing than it was before.**

Example   Calculate the new molarity of hydrochloric acid in each case when 20 cm^3 of 4 M HCl(aq) are added to:
i.   10 cm^3 of water,
ii.   20 cm^3 of 2 M NaCl(aq).

Adding to 10 cm^3 of water

We *could* work from first principles, arguing that:

moles of HCl = molarity × volume (in dm^3) = $4 \times 0.02 = 0.08$

After adding 10 cm^3 of water, this exists in 30 cm^3.

If 30 cm^3 contains 0.08 mol of HCl,
then   1 cm^3 contains $0.08 \div 30 = 2.67 \times 10^{-3}$ mol of HCl,
and   1 dm^3 contains $2.67 \times 10^{-3} \times 1000 = 2.67$ mol of HCl, i.e. the new acid is 2.67 M.

However, it is much more elegant to use what chemists call a *dilution factor*. The new molarity must be derived from the original molarity multiplied by a factor which depends on the original volume of acid and the final volume

$$\text{i.e. new molarity} = 4 \times \frac{20}{30} = 2.67 \text{ M}$$

The dilution factor must be less than 1 because the new molarity is less than the original. Hence,

$$\text{dilution factor} = \frac{\text{original volume of acid solution}}{\text{final volume of acid solution}}$$

First ask yourself, "Will a chemical reaction occur between the two solutes?" The answer, here, is, "No! Hydrochloric acid and sodium chloride do not react together." Consequently, adding 20 cm³ of 2 M NaCl(aq) to 20 cm³ of 4 M HCl(aq) has exactly the same effect as adding 20 cm³ of water.

In other words, the volume of the acid solution is doubled; therefore its concentration is halved, from 4 M to 2 M. (If you are unhappy with this logic, please work through the calculation using either of the methods immediately above.)

Incidentally, the volume of the sodium chloride solution is also doubled when the hydrochloric acid is introduced, so *its* concentration is also halved, from 2 M to 1 M.

Question 3 What is the molar concentration of sulphate ions in an aqueous solution of the double salt commonly called "alum", $K_2SO_4.Al_2(SO_4)_3.24H_2O$, of concentration 189.6 g dm^{-3}.
A_r: H = 1; O = 16; Al = 27; S = 32; K = 39.

Hints First work out the M_r of alum and hence the molar concentration of the solution. Then consider the dissociation equations:

$$K_2SO_4(s) + aq \rightleftharpoons 2K^+(aq) + SO_4^{2-}(aq)$$

$$Al_2(SO_4)_3(s) + aq \rightleftharpoons 2Al^{3+}(aq) + 3SO_4^{2-}(aq)$$

Use these to work out the sulphate ion concentration, first from the potassium sulphate solution and then from the aluminium sulphate; finally, add them together.

Answers to questions in this chapter

1. 0.0989 g Sr; 0.0798 g Cl   2. 2.21 g   3. 0.8 M

Chapter 9

YIELD CALCULATIONS

Mention 'mole calculations' and most people immediately think of yield calculations. It is only natural that a chemist should want to know the *theoretical yield* of a reaction, i.e. how much product could be obtained if everything went smoothly in a perfect world. In practice, of course, what is commonly called 'Murphy's law' applies: "If something *can* go wrong, it *will* go wrong"; consequently, the amount of product obtained (the *actual yield*) is usually less than the theoretical yield. More of this later.

Theoretical Yield Calculations

Reactions involving one reactant only
The procedure is as follows. You will find that it involves no new principles; only the application of those that we have already met.

i. **Write down the correctly balanced chemical equation.**
ii. **Underneath, write "We have ....", followed by the mass of reactant.**
iii. **Convert the mass of reactant into an amount in moles.**
iv. **Referring to the equation, write down the number of moles of product. *Remember that the mole ratio in which substances react is exactly the same as the molecular ratio shown by the equation.***
v. **Finally, convert moles of product into a mass.**

Example Calculate the mass of lead(II) oxide which could be formed by heating 165.5 g of lead(II) nitrate. A_r: N = 14; O = 16; Pb = 207.

The following model answer shows how the procedure operates.

i. The equation is as follows: $2Pb(NO_3)_2 \rightarrow 2PbO + 4NO_2 + O_2$

ii. We have 165.5 g $Pb(NO_3)_2$, of M_r 331.

iii. This is $165.5 \div 331 = 0.5$ mol $Pb(NO_3)_2$.

iv. The equation shows that 2 mol $Pb(NO_3)_2$ gives 2 mol PbO,
    $\therefore$ 0.5 mol $Pb(NO_3)_2$ gives 0.5 mol PbO, of M_r 223.

v. Theoretical yield of PbO $= 0.5 \times 223 = 111.5$ g.

Question 1 By similar reasoning, work out the masses of NO_2 and O_2 which are formed at the same time. When you have finished, check that the total mass of PbO, NO_2 and O_2 = 165.5g. According to the *Law of Conservation of Mass*, matter can be neither created nor destroyed; hence, when a chemical reaction occurs, the mass of products is equal to that of reactants.

Reactions involving two or more reactants

Relatively few chemical reactions involve only one reactant; generally there are two, but there could be more. In such cases, if they are mixed together in the molar ratio shown by the equation, the yield calculation can successfully be based on either (or any) of the reactants.

Example How much sodium nitrate could be formed by mixing together 31.5 g of nitric acid and 20.0 g of sodium hydroxide? A_r: H = 1;   N = 14;   O = 16;   Na = 23.

$$HNO_3 \; + \; NaOH \; \rightarrow \; NaNO_3 \; + \; H_2O$$

We have: 31.5 g   20.0 g

The M_r of HNO_3 is 63 and that of NaOH is 40,

∴   we have 31.5 ÷ 63 mol HNO_3 and 20 ÷ 40 mol NaOH
= 0.5 mol HNO_3 + 0.5 mol NaOH

The reactants are therefore present in a 1:1 ratio as required by the equation. Consequently, you could argue in two ways, both of which would lead you to the same conclusion.

i.   The equation shows that 1 mol HNO_3 gives 1 mol $NaNO_3$,
∴   0.5 mol HNO_3 gives 0.5 mol $NaNO_3$, of M_r 85,
∴   theoretical yield of $NaNO_3$ = 0.5 × 85 = 42.5 g.

ii.   The equation shows that 1 mol NaOH gives 1 mol $NaNO_3$,
∴   0.5 mol NaOH gives 0.5 mol $NaNO_3$ = 42.5 g (as above).

However, what would happen if you were to mix together, say, 20.0 g of sodium hydroxide and 131.5 g of nitric acid? Would the yield of sodium nitrate still be 42.5 g by the second argument, or could you adapt the first argument as follows?

We have 131.5 g HNO_3, corresponding to 131.5 ÷ 63 = 2.09 mol HNO_3,
∴   2.09 mol HNO_3 will give 2.09 mol $NaNO_3$, of M_r 85,
∴   theoretical yield of $NaNO_3$ = 2.09 × 85 = 177.7 g.

A politician would doubtless argue the latter. I'm sure you can picture the scene: "My friends, I am giving you a lot more nitric acid, so you will all get a lot more sodium nitrate." But this is false logic. You certainly would get more product if you were also to increase the mass of sodium hydroxide; otherwise not. So here the yield of sodium nitrate remains at 42.5 g. You cannot possibly exceed this because there is no more sodium hydroxide with which the extra nitric acid can react. The nitric acid is said to be *in excess*; the surplus remains in its original state and serves only to contaminate the product. The yield is controlled by sodium hydroxide which, because there is not enough of it, is referred to as the *deficient* reactant.

Whenever two (or more) substances react together, and one of them is deficient, it is the deficient substance which controls the yield, and the calculation of yield must be based on this.

It is often clear from the question which reactant is in excess and which is deficient.

Example   Sodium hydroxide pellets, when exposed to the atmosphere, absorb carbon dioxide and water so that they are converted, eventually, into sodium carbonate monohydrate. What mass of the latter would be formed from 10.0 g of sodium hydroxide? A_r: H = 1;   C = 12;   O = 16;   Na = 23.

$$2NaOH(s) + CO_2(g) \rightarrow Na_2CO_3(s) + H_2O(l)$$

The question implies that there is enough carbon dioxide and water vapour present to ensure that all the sodium hydroxide reacts. (In general, if ever the amount of a reactant is not stated, it is safe to assume it is present in excess.) Hence, the yield calculation is based on sodium hydroxide. You must remember to take water of crystallisation into account in all calculations involving salt hydrates. Here, we are not preparing anhydrous sodium carbonate, but the monohydrate which is formed by the absorption of water:

$$Na_2CO_3(s) + H_2O(l) \rightarrow Na_2CO_3.H_2O(s)$$

The overall equation is therefore:

$$2NaOH(s) + CO_2(g) \rightarrow Na_2CO_3.H_2O(s)$$

We have 10.0 g of NaOH of M_r 40,
∴   we have 10.0 ÷ 40 = 0.250 mol NaOH.

The equation shows that 2 mol NaOH give 1 mol $Na_2CO_3.H_2O$,
∴   0.250 mol NaOH gives 0.250 ÷ 2   =   0.125 mol $Na_2CO_3.H_2O$, of M_r 124,
∴   theoretical yield of $Na_2CO_3.H_2O$ =   0.125 × 124 = 15.5 g.

Questions

2   Calculate the mass of anhydrous zinc sulphate that could be obtained by dissolving 10.0 g of zinc in a slight excess of dilute sulphuric acid and heating the resulting solution to dryness.
A_r: H = 1;   O =16;   S = 32;   Zn = 65.4.
Note   The adjective *anhydrous* (literally, "dry") tells you that the zinc sulphate does not have any water of crystallisation.

3   Copper(II) sulphate solution was prepared by boiling 10.0 g of copper(II) oxide, CuO, with dilute sulphuric acid until no more would dissolve, and then filtering off unreacted CuO. The latter, after washing and drying, weighed 3.47 g.   What is the maximum mass of copper(II) sulphate pentahydrate, $CuSO_4.5H_2O$, which could be obtained by crystallising the solution?
A_r: H = 1;   O = 16;   S = 32;   Cu = 63.5.

If it is not immediately obvious which reactant is deficient, a simple calculation will decide.

Example Calculate the mass of gaseous hydrogen chloride that could be produced when 73.0 g of pure sulphuric acid are allowed to react with 50.0 g of sodium chloride at room temperature. A_r: H = 1;   O = 16;   Na = 23;   S = 32;   Cl = 35.5.

The equation is: $NaCl + H_2SO_4 \rightarrow NaHSO_4 + HCl$

We have 50.0 g NaCl, of M_r 58.5, and 73.0 g H_2SO_4, of M_r 98,

∴   we have 50.0 ÷ 58.5   = 0.855 mol NaCl

and 73.0 ÷ 98   = 0.745 mol H_2SO_4.

The equation shows that 1 mol NaCl *needs* 1 mol H_2SO_4

∴   0.855 mol NaCl needs 0.855 mol H_2SO_4. This is the *theoretical requirement*, and you must compare it with what you actually have in the laboratory. Here, you are only given 0.745 mol H_2SO_4, so there is not enough of it. NaCl is in excess; **H_2SO_4 is deficient and therefore controls the yield.** Now go back to the equation.

1 mol H_2SO_4 gives 1 mol HCl,

∴   0.745 mol H_2SO_4 gives 0.745 mol HCl, of M_r 36.5,

∴   theoretical yield of HCl = 0.745 × 36.5 = 27.2 g

There is a terrible trap for the unwary in calculations of this kind. It is very tempting to look at the amounts of reactants - in the above question, 0.855 mol NaCl and 0.745 mol H_2SO_4 - and to say, "0.855 mol is greater than 0.745 mol, so obviously NaCl is in excess and H_2SO_4 is deficient." However, unless you refer to the equation, as I did when I said that "1 mol NaCl *needs* 1 mol H_2SO_4", you can so easily jump to the wrong conclusion.

Example Calculate the mass of anhydrous sodium sulphate, Na_2SO_4, that could be obtained by reacting sodium hydroxide solution, containing 35.0 g NaOH, with dilute sulphuric acid containing 49.0 g H_2SO_4. A_r: H = 1;   O = 16;   Na = 23;   S = 32.

The equation is: $2NaOH + H_2SO_4 \rightarrow Na_2SO_4 + 2H_2O$

We have 35.0 g NaOH, of M_r 40, and 49.0 g H_2SO_4 of M_r 98,

∴   we have 35.0 ÷ 40 = 0.875 mol NaOH

and 49.0 ÷ 98 = 0.500 mol H_2SO_4.

It is all too easy to then say, "0.875 mol is greater than 0.500 mol, so obviously NaOH is in excess." But wait; **we must refer to the equation at this stage.** This shows that:

2 mol NaOH *needs* 1 mol H_2SO_4,

∴   0.875 mol NaOH needs 0.875 ÷ 2 = 0.438 mol H_2SO_4.

Comparing this theoretical requirement with what we are using in the laboratory, 0.500 mol H_2SO_4, we see that there is actually an excess of H_2SO_4! NaOH is deficient and controls the yield. See if you can finish off this calculation; the correct answer is 124 g.

To summarise, the procedure is as follows.

i.   **Work out moles of each reagent.**
ii.   **Using the equation, which gives the mole ratio of reactants, calculate the theoretical requirement.** (You can calculate *either* the number of moles of B required to react with so-many moles of A, *or* the number of moles of A needed to react with so-many moles of B. It does not affect the outcome.)
iii.   **Compare the theoretical requirement with the actual amounts present to decide which reactant is deficient.**
iv.   **Finally, carry out a yield calculation in the usual way.**

Question 4   Calculate the mass of anhydrous zinc sulphate that could be obtained by dissolving 10.0 g of zinc in dilute sulphuric acid made by dissolving 13.8 g of the pure acid in water.
(Use the same A_r values as in *Question 2*, and compare your answers!)

Reactions involving gases
        Do not be afraid of these! They are exactly the same as ordinary yield calculations, except that in the final stage you have to convert moles of a gaseous product into a volume instead of a mass. If the gas volume refers to standard conditions (s.t.p.), assume that one mole of any gas occupies 22.4 dm^3. (The examiner will probably tell you this.)

Example   What volume of oxygen at s.t.p. can be obtained by the thermal decomposition of 3.40 g of sodium nitrate? A_r: N = 14; O = 16; Na = 23.

$$2NaNO_3 \rightarrow 2NaNO_2 + O_2$$

We have 3.40 g $NaNO_3$, of M_r 85
This is 3.40 ÷ 85 = 0.0400 mol $NaNO_3$

The equation shows that 2 mol $NaNO_3$ give 1 mol O_2,
∴   0.0400 mol $NaNO_3$ gives 0.0400 ÷ 2 = 0.0200 mol O_2.

If 1 mol O_2 occupies a volume of 22.4 dm^3 at s.t.p.,
then   0.0200 mol O_2 occupies a volume of 22.4 × 0.0200 = 0.448 dm^3.

If the gas volume relates to non-standard conditions, typically room temperature and pressure, you will probably be given the conversion factor.

Example   In one process for the extraction of copper, copper(I) sulphide obtained from the ore copper pyrites is roasted in air so that some of it is converted into copper(I) oxide. This reacts with unconverted copper(I) sulphide to give copper. The reactions which occur are:

$$2Cu_2S + 3O_2 \rightarrow 2Cu_2O + 2SO_2$$
$$2Cu_2O + Cu_2S \rightarrow 6Cu + SO_2$$

What volume (in m^3) of sulphur dioxide would be released in the complete processing of 10 kg of copper(I) sulphide? (Assume that 1 mol of sulphur dioxide occupies 2.40×10^{-2} m^3 at room temperature and atmospheric pressure.) A_r: O = 16; S = 32; Cu = 63.5.

The question refers to the "complete process", so we need to add the given equations together so as to get an overall equation:

$$3Cu_2S + 3O_2 \rightarrow 6Cu + 3SO_2$$

Assume that there is enough air for sufficient Cu_2S to react.

We have 10.0 kg Cu_2S = 10×10^3 g Cu_2S, of M_r 159.
This is $10 \times 10^3 \div 159$ = 62.9 mol Cu_2S.

The equation shows that 3 mol Cu_2S give 3 mol SO_2,
∴   62.9 mol Cu_2S give 62.9 mol SO_2.

If 1 mol SO_2 occupies a volume of 2.40×10^{-2} m^3,
then   62.9 mol SO_2 occupies a volume of $2.40 \times 10^{-2} \times 62.9$ = 1.51 m^3.

If ever you are not given the conversion factor, the number of moles of the gaseous product will have to be converted to a volume by means of the general gas equation (*Chapter 5*). Not all Boards require this.

Questions
5   Sodium hydroxide and ammonium chloride react together as follows:

$$NaOH + NH_4Cl \rightarrow NaCl + NH_3 + H_2O$$

If 10.0 g of sodium hydroxide are heated with 10.7 g of ammonium chloride, calculate:
 a) the maximum mass of ammonia that can be obtained;
 b) the volume (in dm^3) of gaseous ammonia at s.t.p.;
 c) the volume (in dm^3) of gaseous ammonia at 20 °C (293 K) and 95 kPa (95 000 Nm^{-2}).
$R = 8.31$ $JK^{-1}mol^{-1}$. Molar volume of a gas at s.t.p. = 22.4 dm^3.
A_r: H = 1; N = 14; O = 16; Na = 23; Cl = 35.5.
6   Calculate the mass of steam produced when 10 dm^3 of hydrogen are exploded with 4 dm^3 of oxygen. (Both volumes relate to s.t.p. Use the data in *Question 5*.)

Short cuts for multi-stage reactions

When a question relates to the final yield of a multi-stage synthesis, it is usually unnecessary to calculate the yields at intermediate stages.

Example How much lead(II) sulphide can be obtained from 1.00 g of lead by the following series of reactions? A_r: S = 32; Pb = 207.

i. Dissolving lead in dilute nitric acid:

$$Pb \; + \; 4HNO_3 \; \rightarrow \; Pb(NO_3)_2 \; + \; 2NO_2 \; + \; 2H_2O$$

ii. Evaporating to dryness and further heating to decompose the lead(II) nitrate:

$$2Pb(NO_3)_2 \; \rightarrow \; 2PbO \; + \; 4NO_2 \; + \; O_2$$

iii. Dissolving the residue of lead(II) oxide in ethanoic acid:

$$PbO \; + \; 2CH_3COOH \; \rightarrow \; (CH_3COO)_2Pb \; + \; H_2O$$

iv. Passing hydrogen sulphide gas through the solution:

$$(CH_3COO)_2Pb \; + \; H_2S \; \rightarrow \; PbS \; + \; 2CH_3COOH$$

It is possible to calculate, first, the mass of lead(II) nitrate, and then in turn the masses of lead(II) oxide, lead(II) ethanoate and lead(II) sulphide, but this time-consuming and unnecessary. If you look at the chemical equations you will see that, provided there is an excess of reagents, one mole of metallic lead is eventually converted into one mole of lead(II) sulphide. No lead is lost in the formation of other products.

$$1Pb \; \equiv \; 1Pb(NO_3)_2 \; \equiv \; 1PbO \; \equiv \; 1(CH_3COO)_2Pb \; \equiv \; 1PbS$$

We have 1.0 g of lead, corresponding to $1 \div 207 \; = \; 4.83 \times 10^{-3}$ mol Pb.

Since 1 mol Pb gives 1 mol PbS,
then 4.83×10^{-3} mol Pb gives 4.83×10^{-3} mol PbS, of M_r 239,
$\therefore$ theoretical yield of PbS $= \; 4.83 \times 10^{-3} \times 239 \; = \; 1.15$ g

Reactions on an industrial scale

Where large amounts of substances are involved it is often inconvenient to work in grams. Kilograms or tonnes may be more sensible, in which case the easiest approach is to scale things up from grams to kilograms or tonnes (as appropriate) by simply changing the units.

Example Aluminium is manufactured by the electrolysis of purified bauxite, Al_2O_3, in molten cryolite. Calculate the mass of aluminium which could be produced from 1 tonne of Al_2O_3. A_r: O = 16; Al = 27.

Essentially, aluminium oxide is decomposed by electricity into its elements, a process represented by the equation:

$$2Al_2O_3 \; \rightarrow \; 4Al \; + \; 3O_2$$

You *could* work in the usual way. There is 1 t of Al_2O_3 = 1×10^6 g Al_2O_3, of M_r 102. This corresponds to $1 \times 10^6 \div 102$ = 9804 mol Al_2O_3.

The equation shows that 2 mol Al_2O_3 give 4 mol Al,

∴   1 mol Al_2O_3 gives 2 mol Al,

∴   9804 mol Al_2O_3 give 2×9804 = 19608 mol Al, of A_r 27,

∴   theoretical yield of Al = 19608×27 = 529416 g = 0.529 t.

However, a much neater way is to switch from grams to tonnes as soon as possible.

The equation shows that 1 mol Al_2O_3 (M_r = 102) gives 2 mol Al (A_r = 27),

∴   102 g Al_2O_3 give 2×27 = 54 g Al,

∴   102 t Al_2O_3 give 54 t Al,

∴   1 t Al_2O_3 gives $54 \div 102$ = 0.529 t Al.

Percentage Yield Calculations

When you carry out chemical reactions you will generally find that the actual yield is less than the theoretical yield. The main reasons for this are as follows.

i.   *The reaction may not proceed to completion.*
Some reactions are reversible, in which case the products tend to revert to the original substances. Complete conversion is impossible and an equilibrium mixture is obtained.

ii.   *Handling losses.*
Some material always adheres to the apparatus in which it is made.

iii.   *Vaporisation losses.*
A certain amount of a volatile liquid or solid will always escape to atmosphere even though it may be kept in a stoppered bottle or flask.

iv.   *Crystallisation losses.*
A dissolved substance is usually recovered from solution by crystallisation, an excellent technique except that some of the substance remains in solution and is lost.

v.   *Side reactions.*
Sometimes more than one reaction can occur under a given set of conditions. The reactions are said to compete against each other. Those which occur to a small extent are known as *side reactions* and, because they consume some of the reactants, they lead to a lowering of yield in the main reaction.

A measure of the efficiency of a preparation is provided by the *percentage yield*, which is defined as follows:

$$\text{percentage yield} = \frac{\text{actual yield}}{\text{theoretical yield}} \times 100$$

The units in this calculation are generally grams, although others may be used for convenience. What *is* important is that the units are the same in both numerator and denominator. The calculation should always relate to the purified product; never to crude material.

50

Example When benzenecarboxylic acid was prepared by the alkaline hydrolysis of 5.00 g of its ester, ethyl benzenecarboxylate, followed by acidification with dilute hydrochloric acid, only 2.73 g of benzenecarboxylic acid were obtained because some of it remained in solution. Calculate the percentage yield. A_r: $H = 1$; $C = 12$; $O = 16$.

The equations for the reactions are:

$$C_6H_5COOC_2H_5 + NaOH \rightarrow C_6H_5COONa + C_2H_5OH$$
$$C_6H_5COONa + HCl \rightarrow C_6H_5COOH + H_2O$$

We have 5.00 g of ethyl benzenecarboxylate, of M_r 150.

This corresponds to $5.00 \div 150 = 0.0333$ mol ethyl benzenecarboxylate.

The equation shows that 1 mol of ethyl benzenecarboxylate gives 1 mol of sodium benzenecarboxylate, which in turn gives 1 mol of benzenecarboxylic acid,

∴   0.0333 mol of the ester gives 0.0333 mol of the acid, of M_r 122,

∴   theoretical yield of benzenecarboxylic acid $= 0.0333 \times 122 = 4.07$ g,

∴   percentage yield of the acid $= \dfrac{2.73}{4.07} \times 100 = 67.1\%$

Questions

7   In a multi-stage synthesis, 9.20 g of methylbenzene, $C_6H_5CH_3$, were converted into 1.80 g of aspirin, $C_6H_4(OCOCH_3)COOH$. Calculate the percentage yield. A_r: $H = 1$; $C = 12$; $O = 16$.

8   Nitrobenzene was reduced to phenylamine and then converted to phenol by diazotisation followed by hydrolysis:

$$C_6H_5NO_2 + 6[H] \rightarrow C_6H_5NH_2 + 2H_2O$$

$$C_6H_5NH_2 + NaNO_2 + 2HCl \rightarrow C_6H_5N\equiv N^+ \, Cl^- + NaCl + 2H_2O$$

$$C_6H_5N\equiv N^+ \, Cl^- + H_2O \rightarrow C_6H_5OH + HCl + N_2$$

Starting from 10.0 g of nitrobenzene, 2.18 g of phenol were obtained. What was the percentage yield? A_r: $H = 1$; $C = 12$; $N = 14$; $O = 16$.

9   In an experiment to prepare calcium nitrate tetrahydrate, 10.0 g of calcium carbonate were dissolved in a slight excess of dilute nitric acid. The resulting solution was concentrated by boiling in an evaporating basin and then set aside to cool. Unfortunately, it did not crystallise well and only 4.28 g of $Ca(NO_3)_2.4H_2O$ were obtained. What was the percentage yield? A_r: $H = 1$; $N = 14$; $O = 16$; $Ca = 40$.

Answers to questions in this chapter

1. 46.0 g NO_2; 8.0 g O_2 2. 24.7 g   3. 20.5 g   4. 22.7 g   5. a) 3.40 g; b) 4.48 dm^3; c) 5.13 dm^3 6. 6.43 g   7. 10.0%   8. 28.5%   9 18.1%

Chapter 10

CALCULATING REACTING MASSES

A variation on the "How much product is formed?" type of calculation is the sort that reads "How much reactant (or reactants) is (or are) needed to form a given quantity of product?" This is probably the commonest type of calculation in everyday chemistry, because it must be carried out by a chemist before any preparation can be carried out either in the laboratory or in industry.

The procedure for calculating reacting masses is almost the same as that for calculating yields. The only real difference is that, instead of writing down "We have..." at the start of the calculation, you must write down "We need...". The complete routine is therefore as follows.

i. **Write down the correctly balanced chemical equation.**
ii. **Underneath, write "We *need* ...", followed by the given mass of the *product*.**
iii. **Convert the mass of product into an amount in moles.**
iv. **Referring to the equation, write down the number of moles of reactant. *Remember* (as before) *that the mole ratio in which substances react is the same as the molecular ratio shown by the equation.***
v. **Finally, convert moles of reactant into a mass.**

Example Calculate the mass of aluminium hydroxide that must be heated in order to obtain 10.0 g of aluminium oxide. A_r: H = 1; O = 16; Al = 27.

i. The equation is as follows:
$$2Al(OH)_3 \rightarrow Al_2O_3 + 3H_2O$$

ii. We *need* 10.0 g Al_2O_3, of M_r 102.

iii. This is 10.0 ÷ 102 = 0.0980 mol Al_2O_3.

iv. The equation shows that 1 mol Al_2O_3 needs 2 mol $Al(OH)_3$,
∴ 0.0980 mol Al_2O_3 needs 0.0980 × 2 = 0.196 mol $Al(OH)_3$, of M_r 78.
v. Theoretical requirement of $Al(OH)_3$ = 0.196 × 78 = 15.3 g.

Current examinations often place such questions in an industrial context. If the masses are high, it will pay you to scale up from grams to kilograms or even tonnes by changing the units, as described in the previous chapter.

Example Copper can be recovered from copper(II) sulphate by a displacement reaction using scrap iron. How many tonnes of iron would be required to recover 10 tonnes of copper?
A_r: Fe = 56; Cu = 63.5.

The equation is: $Fe(s) + CuSO_4(aq) \rightarrow FeSO_4(aq) + Cu(s)$

This shows that 1 mol Cu (A_r = 63.5) needs 1 mol Fe (A_r = 56),
∴ 63.5 g Cu need 56 g Fe,
∴ 63.5 t Cu need 56 t Fe,
∴ 1 t Cu needs 56 ÷ 63.5 = 0.882 t Fe,
∴ 10 t Cu ned 0.882 × 10 = 8.82 t Fe.

When doing yield calculations for multi-stage syntheses, we saw that it was generally unnecessary to calculate the yield at intermediate stages. So, here, you can usually omit intermediates.

Example   Titanium is manufactured by the Kroll process, which is operated in two stages. First, chlorine is passed over a heated mixture of titanium(IV) oxide and carbon to produce titanium(IV) chloride:

$$2TiO_2 \ + \ 3C \ + \ 4Cl_2 \ \rightarrow \ 2TiCl_4 \ + \ 2CO \ + \ CO_2$$

Titanium(IV) chloride, after purification, is then reduced *in vacuo* with a more reactive metal such as sodium:

$$TiCl_4 \ + \ 4Na \ \rightarrow \ Ti \ + \ 4NaCl$$

What mass of titanium(IV) oxide would be required to produce 2.5 tonnes of titanium?
A_r: O = 16;   Ti = 48.

If you multiply the second equation throughout by two, and then add it to the first, $TiCl_4$ cancels out and you get an overall equation:

$$2TiO_2 + 3C + 4Cl_2 + 8Na \ \rightarrow \ 2Ti \ + \ 8NaCl \ + \ 2CO \ + \ CO_2$$

This shows that 2 mol Ti need 2 mol TiO_2,
∴   1 mol Ti (A_r = 48) needs 1 mol TiO_2 (M_r = 80),
∴   48 g Ti need 80 g TiO_2, and 48 t Ti need 80 t TiO_2.
∴   1 t Ti needs 80 ÷ 48   = 1.67 t TiO_2,
∴   2.5 t Ti need 1.67 × 2.5 = 4.18 t TiO_2.

Question 1   In the Ostwald process for the production of nitric acid, ammonia is catalytically oxidised by air to nitrogen monoxide:

$$4NH_3(g) \ + \ 5O_2(g) \ \rightarrow \ 4NO(g) \ + \ 6H_2O(g) \qquad \textit{Equation 1}$$

On cooling, excess air oxidises the nitrogen monoxide to nitrogen dioxide:

$$2NO(g) \ + \ O_2(g) \ \rightarrow \ 2NO_2(g) \qquad \textit{Equation 2}$$

Finally, nitrogen dioxide is absorbed in water in the presence of air. Several reactions occur, as a result of which virtually all the nitrogen dioxide is converted into nitric acid:

$$4NO_2(g) \ + \ 2H_2O(l) \ + \ O_2(g) \ \rightarrow \ 4HNO_3(aq) \qquad \textit{Equation 3}$$

Calculate the number of moles of ammonia needed to produce one mole of nitric acid.

When doing industrial questions, you should bear in mind that the substances employed are often impure, so that more than the theoretical amount may be needed.

Example   Calculate the volume of air required to oxidise 1 m^3 of ammonia to nitrogen monoxide in the first stage of the Ostwald process. (Assume that air consists of 20% of oxygen (by volume) and 80% of nitrogen.)

Equation 1 shows that 4 molecules NH_3 need 5 molecules O_2. Bearing in mind that, for gas reactions, the volume ratio is the same as the molecular ratio,
then   4 m^3 NH_3 need 5 m^3 O_2,
∴   1 m^3 NH_3 needs 5 ÷ 4 = 1.25 m^3 O_2.

However, since air is only one-fifth O_2, we need five times as much air as oxygen,
i.e.   1 m^3 NH_3 needs 1.25 × 5 = 6.25 m^3 air.

Question 2   A blast furnace is designed to produce 750 tonnes of iron per day by the reduction of haematite. Calculate the mass of haematite needed to reach this production target, given that the ore contains only 75% of Fe_2O_3. *A_r:* $O = 16$; $Fe = 56$.

In some questions you may be asked to calculate the mass of one reactant required to combine with a given mass of another. The procedure is exactly the same as before.

Example   A road tanker has crashed on a motorway, spilling 1000 dm^3 of 10 M hydrochloric acid. What is the minimum mass of calcium carbonate which the fire brigade would need to neutralise this acid? *A_r:* $C = 12$; $O = 16$; $Ca = 40$.

Amount of HCl spilt = molarity $\times$ volume (in dm^3) = 10×1000 = 10 000 mol.
The equation is: $CaCO_3 + 2HCl \rightarrow CaCl_2 + H_2O + CO_2$
This shows that 2 mol HCl need 1 mol CaCO $_3$,
∴.   1 mol HCl needs 0.5 mol $CaCO_3$,
∴.   10 000 mol HCl need $0.5 \times 10\,000 =$ 5000 mol $CaCO_3$, of M_r 100,
∴.   theoretical requirement of CaCO $_3$ = 5000×100 = 500 000 g = 500 kg.

Question 3 During steel making, sulphur is removed from molten crude iron by adding magnesium. This converts it to magnesium sulphide:

$$Mg + S \rightarrow MgS$$

If a certain 100 tonne batch of crude iron contains 0.35% of sulphur, how many kilograms of magnesium would be required to remove the sulphur? *A_r:* $Mg = 24$; $S = 32$.

Answers to questions in this chapter
1. 1 mol   2. 1429 t   3. 263 kg

ACID-BASE TITRATIONS

Volumetric analysis is essentially a means of estimating the concentration of one solution, given that of another, by comparing the volume ratio in which they react. Various kinds of reactions can be used as the basis of volumetric analysis, namely:

i.   acid-base reactions, where an acid is titrated against a base (or vice versa);
ii.   redox reactions, where an oxidising agent is titrated against a reducing agent;
iii.   precipitation reactions, where a halide (usually a chloride) is titrated against silver nitrate;
iv.   complex formation, where a metal salt solution is titrated against edta.

All employ different *indicators*, i.e. coloured substances which tell you when you have reached the *equivalence point*, where the reactants are present in the molar proportions shown in the chemical equation. Careful selection of indicator is essential to ensure that the *end-point* of the titration (where the indicator changes colour) corresponds to the equivalence point: this aspect is taught in Physical Chemistry.

Volumetric analysis is thus a very flexible analytical method; a great many substances can be estimated in this way. Whatever kind of reaction is involved, the working out of results is always essentially the same, and based on the type of calculation we met in the previous chapter. The only difference is that, instead of calculating reacting masses, we have the job of calculating reacting concentrations or, in some cases, reacting volumes. In this chapter we shall see how the principles are applied to acid-base reactions: in later chapters the identical principles will be applied to other sorts of titrations.

The first thing you must do, before tackling any volumetric analysis calculation, is to **write down the balanced chemical equation for the reaction which is taking place.** This is essential because it tells you the mole ratio in which the reactants (here, acid and base) react together. *It is vital to write down the ratio clearly,* because:

i.   you cannot possibly do the calculation without it;
ii.   the examiner will be looking for this ratio, and it could well carry a mark.

Example 25.0 cm^3 of 0.0543 M sodium carbonate solution (measured with a pipette) neutralised 23.5 cm^3 of dilute hydrochloric acid (run in from a burette). Calculate the molarity (i.e. concentration in mol dm^{-3}) of the hydrochloric acid.

The equation for the reaction is

$$2HCl + Na_2CO_3 \rightarrow 2NaCl + H_2O + CO_2$$

We *could* argue that:

amount (in mol) of Na_2CO_3 = molarity × volume (in dm^3)
= 0.0543 × 0.025 = 1.36 × 10^{-3} mol
The equation shows that:

1 mol Na_2CO_3 needs 2 mol HCl,
∴   1.36 × 10^{-3} mol Na_2CO_3 need 2 × 1.36 × 10^{-3} = 2.72 × 10^{-3} mol HCl.

Remember that this is in 23.5 cm^3 (0.0235 dm^3) of hydrochloric acid.

Amount (in mol) of HCl $=$ molarity $\times$ volume (in dm^3),

$\therefore$ $\quad$ 2.72×10^{-3} $=$ M(HCl) $\times$ 0.0235

$\therefore$ $\quad$ M(HCl) $=$ $(2.72 \times 10^{-3}) \div 0.0235$ $=$ 0.116 M

This is a very common way of teaching the topic, and the examiner could well lead you through a structured calculation in this way, but, *given a free hand*, you may find it quicker to argue as follows:

$$\frac{\text{moles of acid (HCl)}}{\text{moles of base (Na}_2\text{CO}_3)} = \frac{2}{1} \qquad\qquad \textit{Equation 1}$$

$\therefore$
$$\frac{\text{molarity} \times \text{volume (in dm}^3) \text{ of HCl}}{\text{molarity} \times \text{volume (in dm}^3) \text{ of Na}_2\text{CO}_3} = \frac{2}{1} \qquad\qquad \textit{Equation 2}$$

$\therefore$
$$\frac{\text{M(HCl)} \times 0.02350}{0.0543 \times 0.0250} = \frac{2}{1}$$

Rearranging this equation by the method of cross-multiplication (*Chapter 4*),

$$\text{M(HCl)} = \frac{2 \times 0.0543 \times 0.0250}{1 \times 0.02350} = 0.116 \text{ M}$$

Both methods of setting out these calculations are in common use and, if you ask which is preferable, the answer must be that you should adopt the method which *you* prefer. In this book I shall use the second approach, not just for speed but also because, working with molarities, you are less likely to make mistakes. (The snag with the first method is that you must always keep asking yourself the question, "Moles in what volume?") However, I must emphasise that, if you have been taught a method which you like and understand, *you should stick to it*. There is never any point in changing horses in mid-stream!

Notes on the change from Equation 1 to Equation 2 - see above

i. If you are given the volume of a solution, or if you are required to calculate a volume, the substitution for "moles" of "molarity $\times$ volume" will be helpful.

ii. If you are not given a volume, but instead told the amount of a substance in moles, *do not make this substitution.* **You are never entitled to invent a volume!**

iii. If you do replace "moles" by "molarity $\times$ volume", this does not necessarily have to be done at both the top and the bottom. Do what is most convenient: you have a lot of flexibility.

Questions

1 $\quad$ In a titration with methyl orange as the indicator, 25.0 cm^3 of sodium hydroxide solution required 27.85 cm^3 of 0.0487 M sulphuric acid to produce a colour change. Calculate the molarity of the sodium hydroxide solution.

2 $\quad$ Calculate the volume of 0.0990 M sodium hydroxide solution required to neutralise a solution containing 0.148 g of pure ethanoic acid. A_r: H = 1; C = 12; O = 16.

Hint $\quad$ Although a molecule of ethanoic acid has four hydrogen atoms, only one of these (that bonded to oxygen) is replaced by a metal atom in neutralisation reactions. The equation is:

$$CH_3COOH + NaOH \rightarrow CH_3COONa + H_2O$$

Variations

Questions in which the molarity of the primary standard must first be calculated

In every titration, the solution to be estimated is titrated with a standard solution (i.e. one of known molarity) of a primary standard. A *primary standard* is a reliable starting material; a solid compound which is readily available in a high state of purity and which does not deteriorate either in the solid state or in solution. For acid-base titrations, the commonest primary standards are anhydrous sodium carbonate and ethanedioic acid dihydrate.

In many calculations, you are told how much of the primary standard is weighed out and the volume of the solution it gives on being dissolved in distilled water. From this information, you must calculate the molarity of the primary standard (by the method we used in *Chapter 3*) before attempting the main calculation. Let's work through the following example together.

Example 1.547 g of anhydrous sodium carbonate were dissolved in distilled water and made up to 250 cm^3 in a graduated flask. 25.0 cm^3 of this solution neutralised 24.6 cm^3 of dilute sulphuric acid. Calculate the concentration of the sulphuric acid in grams per dm^3.
A_r: H = 1; C = 12; O = 16; Na = 23; S = 32.

First calculate the concentration of the sodium carbonate in g dm^{-3}. (You should get a figure of 6.19.) Turn this into a molar concentration. (The correct figure is 0.0584 M.)

Now write the chemical equation and inspect it to find the mole ratio of acid to base. Write this in the form of *Equation 1* (p. 56) and then replace "moles" by "molarity × volume" in both the numerator and the denominator. Solve the equation in the usual way and you should get a molarity of 0.0593 for the sulphuric acid. Finally, convert mol dm^{-3} to g dm^{-3} and see if you get the correct answer of 5.81 g dm^{-3}. If you are happy with this, try the next one.

Question 3 Sodium hydroxide is not a primary standard because it is *deliquescent*, i.e it absorbs water vapour from the air and becomes wet. Its solutions must therefore be *standardised* before use, i.e. their exact concentrations have to be found. In one such experiment, 24.1 cm^3 of sodium hydroxide solution were required to neutralise 25.0 cm^3 of a solution prepared by dissolving 1.458 g of ethanedioic acid dihydrate, $H_2C_2O_4.2H_2O$, in water and making up to 250 cm^3. What was the molarity of the NaOH(aq)? A_r: H = 1; C = 12; O = 16.
Hints Do not forget to include water of crystallisation when working out the M_r of ethanedioic acid. Remember that ethanedioic acid is diprotic; see equation on p. 37.

Dilution questions
Whenever you have the task of estimating a concentrated solution, you must begin by diluting that solution by a known amount. If you did not do so, you would need a ridiculously large volume of the other solution, and would probably have to keep stopping the titration in order to refill the burette!

Example 100 cm^3 of concentrated hydrochloric acid were pipetted into a 1 dm^3 graduated flask and diluted to the mark with distilled water. 25.0 cm^3 of this diluted solution were titrated by 23.6 cm^3 of 0.099 M NaOH(aq). What was the molarity of the concentrated hydrochloric acid?

You must start, as always, with the experimental results. Please calculate the molarity of the *diluted* hydrochloric acid. (It should be 0.0935 M.) You then argue that the original acid was ten times more concentrated than this because, in preparing a solution for titration, the concentrated hydrochloric acid was diluted ten times, i.e. from 100 cm^3 to 1000 cm^3. The original acid is therefore 9.35 M.
In general terms, you must multiply the molarity of a diluted solution by a conversion factor,

often called a "scaling-up factor", defined as follows:

$$\text{scaling-up factor} \quad = \quad \frac{\text{volume of diluted solution}}{\text{volume of original solution}}$$

You'll always get this fraction the right way up if you remember that it must be greater than 1.

Here is an interesting question for further practice.

Question 4 In an experiment to determine the ethanoic acid content of vinegar, 25.0 cm^3 of vinegar were diluted to 200 cm^3 with distilled water. 25.0 cm^3 of the diluted solution were titrated by 25.5 cm^3 of 0.102 M NaOH(aq). Calculate:
a) the mass of ethanoic acid in a 350 cm^3 bottle of vinegar;
b) the mass of ethanoic acid in a 1.14 dm^3 bottle of vinegar;
c) the volume of 0.102 M NaOH(aq) which would have been needed to titrate 25.0 cm^3 of the original vinegar. A_r: H = 1; C = 12; O = 16.

Determination of water of crystallisation
In such calculations we compare the concentration of a solution, as found by volumetric analysis, with the concentration of that solution as prepared in the laboratory. Any discrepancy is attributed to water of crystallisation.

Example 1.33 g of hydrated ethanedioic acid, $H_2C_2O_4.nH_2O$, were dissolved in distilled water and the solution made up to 250 cm^3 in a graduated flask. 25.0 cm^3 of this solution were titrated by 21.1 cm^3 of 0.100 M NaOH(aq). How many molecules of water of crystallisation are there in the hydrated ethanedioic acid? A_r: H = 1; C = 12; O = 16.

First, work out the molarity of the ethanedioic acid solution from the titration results (0.0422 M). Convert this to a concentration in g dm^{-3} (3.80).

What you have just worked out is the mass per dm^3 of *anhydrous* $H_2C_2O_4$. You must now compare it with the concentration of *hydrated* $H_2C_2O_4$. 1.33 g of the hydrated acid were weighed out and made up to $^1/_4$ dm^3,

∴   the concentration of hydrated $H_2C_2O_4$ is 1.33 × 4 = 5.32 g dm^{-3}.

The difference = 5.32 - 3.80 = 1.52 g dm^{-3} is due to H_2O.

This converts to 1.52 ÷ 18 = 0.0844 mol dm^{-3} H_2O.

We can now argue, by simple proportion,

if   0.0422 mol dm^{-3} $H_2C_2O_4$ corresponds to 0.0844 mol dm^{-3} H_2O,
then   1 mol dm^{-3} $H_2C_2O_4$ corresponds to 0.0844 ÷ 0.0422 = 2 mol dm^{-3} H_2O,
i.e.   1 molecule $H_2C_2O_4$ corresponds to 2 molecules H_2O.

To summarise, the procedure is as follows.

i.   Calculate the molarity of the solution.
ii.   Convert to a concentration in g dm^{-3}. (Remember - this figure relates to *anhydrous* compound.)

iii.   Calculate the concentration in g dm^{-3} of hydrated compound. (Look at the question to see how much compound was weighed out and what volume of solution was prepared.)

iv.   Subtract these two concentrations to find g dm^{-3} of H_2O.

v.   Convert to mol dm^{-3} of H_2O.

vi.   Use the figures from i. and v. to find the mole ratio of compound:H_2O.

Question 5   "Washing soda" is hydrated sodium carbonate, $Na_2CO_3.nH_2O$. 4.03 g of this substance were weighed out and dissolved in water to make 250 cm^3 of solution. 25.0 cm^3 of this solution were titrated by 26.6 cm^3 of 0.106 M HCl(aq). Calculate the value of n.
A_r: H = 1;   C = 12;   O = 16;   Na = 23.

Percentage purity

In volumetric methods to determine the purity of compounds it is always assumed that the impurities are inert, in the sense that they do not react with the reagents which are being used. (If ever an impurity *did* react, the method would be invalid and would have to be modified or even changed altogether.) Consequently, the mass of pure compound, as determined by analysis, is always less than the mass of the impure compound which has been weighed out, and we can quote a *percentage purity*, defined as follows:

$$\text{percentage purity} \quad = \quad \frac{\text{mass of pure compound}}{\text{mass of impure compound}} \quad \times \quad 100$$

Example   Calcium hydroxide (agricultural "slaked lime") deteriorates on storage because of the absorption of carbon dioxide from the atmosphere, which slowly converts it into calcium carbonate. In an experiment to determine purity, 0.204 g of slaked lime were weighed out, transferred to a beaker, and sufficient water was then added to dissolve the calcium hydroxide. The insoluble calcium carbonate was filtered off and washed, the washings being added to the main solution. This solution was then titrated by 20.8 cm^3 of 0.210 M HCl(aq). Calculate the percentage purity of the slaked lime.
A_r: H = 1;   O = 16;   Ca = 40.

Write down the equation for the reaction. What is the mole ratio of acid:base? (You should find that it is 2:1.) Now write:

$$\frac{\text{molarity} \times \text{volume (in dm}^3) \text{ of HCl}}{\text{moles of Ca(OH)}_2} \quad = \quad \frac{2}{1}$$

Notice that, in the denominator, we have left "moles" as "moles". We cannot replace it by "molarity × volume" because we are not given the volume of the calcium hydroxide solution.

Calculate moles of Ca(OH)$_2$ (2.18 × 10^{-3}), then mass (0.162 g) and finally purity (79.4%).

In many calculations of percentage purity it is convenient to modify the definition to read:

$$\text{percentage purity} \quad = \quad \frac{\text{g dm}^{-3} \text{ of pure compound}}{\text{g dm}^{-3} \text{ of impure compound}} \quad \times \quad 100$$

Depending on the question, other concentration units may be used. Always make sure the units are consistent!

In a further variation, you may be asked to work out the percentage of an impurity. "Easy," you may say. "Just work out the percentage of the main compound and subtract from 100%." However, such questions can seem very confusing if the "impurity" is, in fact, the principal constituent. In all cases, *you must focus on the compound which is reacting with the volumetric reagent,* even though it may be the minor component.

Both these aspects feature in the next question.

Question 6 A bottle of sodium chloride has become contaminated by sodium carbonate. 5.07 g of the mixture were dissolved in distilled water and made up to 250 cm^3. 25.0 cm^3 of this solution were titrated with 18.6 cm^3 of 0.105 M HCl(aq). Calculate the percentage purity of the sodium chloride.
A_r: C = 12; O = 16; Na = 23.
Hints Sodium chloride does not react with hydrochloric acid. Calculate the molarity of the Na$_2$CO$_3$ in the usual way and convert to g dm^{-3}. Then find the mass of Na$_2$CO$_3$ in 250 cm^3 and hence the percentage of Na$_2$CO$_3$ in the mixture. Finally subtract from 100% to find percentage of NaCl.

Answers to questions in this chapter

1. 0.1085 M   2. 24.9 cm^3 3. 0.0960 M   4. a) 17.5g; b) 56.9 g; c) 204 cm^3 5. 10.0
6. 79.6%

Chapter 12

BACK TITRATIONS

There are some substances which cannot be estimated directly by titration because, unless the reagent is present in excess, the reaction does not go to completion. Obviously, the use of too much volumetric reagent gives a faulty, high result.

In such cases we take a lot of reagent, i.e. more than is needed in theory. Some of the reagent reacts with the compound which is being analysed, while some does not. The reagent which does not react is said to be *in excess*. The amount which is in excess is found by so-called *back titration* with a standard solution of an acid or base.

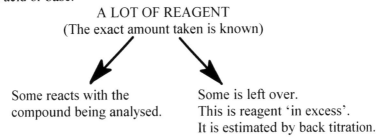

A LOT OF REAGENT
(The exact amount taken is known)

Some reacts with the
compound being analysed.

Some is left over.
This is reagent 'in excess'.
It is estimated by back titration.

If we subtract the amount of reagent in excess from the amount taken, we can easily find the amount which has reacted with the compound being analysed. This is the information which we would have got from direct titration (had it been possible to work accurately!) and from this point onwards the calculation is entirely normal.

At 'A' level there are two principal applications of this technique. One is for the estimation of ammonium salts and the other for the estimation of calcium carbonate.

Estimation Of Ammonium Salts

A known quantity of the ammonium salt is boiled with a relatively large quantity of aqueous sodium hydroxide so that it is completely decomposed, with the liberation of ammonia:

$$NH_4^+(aq) \ + \ OH^-(aq) \ \rightarrow \ NH_3(g) \ + \ H_2O(l)$$

A measured amount of sodium hydroxide solution is used for this purpose. Some reacts with the ammonium salt, while some is left over. This sodium hydroxide 'in excess' is estimated by back titration with a standard solution of an acid.

In your working out of results there are four essential steps. **Try to learn these!**

i.   Calculate the amount (in moles) of sodium hydroxide taken at the start.
ii.   Calculate the amount (in moles) of sodium hydroxide in excess. (Use the results of the back titration for this.)
iii.   Subtract one from the other to find the amount of NaOH which has reacted with the ammonium salt.
iv.   By reference to the equation (for the ammonium salt reacting with NaOH) find out how much ammonium salt is present; or maybe ammonium ions - examiners' requirements vary.

Example   0.975 g of a fertiliser consisting of ammonium sulphate and potassium sulphate was boiled with 10.0 cm^3 of 0.950 M aqueous sodium hydroxide. When no more ammonia was evolved, the residual solution was neutralised by 24.75 cm^3 of 0.0502 M sulphuric acid. Calculate the percentage of ammonium sulphate in the fertiliser. M_r (NH$_4$)$_2$SO$_4$ = 132

Do not be distracted by potassium sulphate. This compound is inert in the sense that it does not react with sodium hydroxide. Treat it as an impurity. In effect, the examiner is asking you to find the percentage purity of ammonium sulphate.

Step 1   Please calculate the amount of NaOH taken. (Your answer should be 9.5×10^{-3} mol.)

Step 2   Now calculate the amount of NaOH in excess. Write down the equation for sulphuric acid reacting with sodium hydroxide, and express the acid:base ratio in the style of *Equation 1* (p. 56). Substitute in this equation to find moles of NaOH. (The right figure is 2.48×10^{-3} mol.)

Step 3   Find the amount of NaOH which has reacted with the ammonium sulphate. Remember - this is just a subtraction. (7.02×10^{-3} mol)

Step 4   Calculate the amount of ammonium sulphate present after completing the equation:

$$(NH_4)_2SO_4 \ + \ NaOH \ \rightarrow$$

in order to find the mole ratio in which these compounds react together. (3.51×10^{-3} mol)

In this question the examiner wants you to express the answer as a percentage, i.e.

$$\frac{\text{mass of ammonium sulphate}}{\text{mass of fertiliser}} \ \times \ 100$$

Thus, all we have to do is convert moles of ammonium sulphate to grams and then substitute:

$$\text{percentage } (NH_4)_2SO_4 \ = \ \frac{3.51 \times 10^{-3} \times 132}{0.975} \ = \ 47.5\%$$

Question 1   0.414 g of an ammonium salt was boiled with 10.0 cm^3 of 1.04 M aqueous sodium hydroxide until no more ammonia was evolved. Afterwards the solution was titrated with 0.101 M hydrochloric acid, 26.25 cm^3 of which were needed to reach an end-point with methyl orange. Calculate the percentage of ammonia in the ammonium salt. A_r: H = 1; N = 14.

Hint   Follow steps 1, 2 & 3 as above to find the amount of NaOH reacting with the ammonium salt. *Step 4* must be modified because the examiner is asking for the percentage of ammonia in an ammonium salt without telling you the identity of that salt. Obviously, we cannot write a molecular equation; but we *can* write an ionic one:

$$NH_4^+(aq) \ + \ OH^-(aq) \ \rightarrow \ NH_3(g) \ + \ H_2O(l)$$

Inspection of this equation shows that n mol of OH$^-$ ions react with n mol of NH$_4^+$ ions to release n mol of NH$_3$, where n can have any value you like. Hence you can find the number of moles of NH$_3$, then its mass, and finally substitute in the equation:

$$\text{ammonia content of salt} \ = \ \frac{\text{mass of ammonia}}{\text{mass of ammonium salt}} \ \times \ 100$$

Note   In some similar questions you are asked to find the nitrogen content of a fertiliser. Just remember that the fraction of nitrogen combined in ammonia = N/NH$_3$ = 14/17.

In some determinations, after the ammonium salt has been boiled with NaOH(aq), only a part of the resulting solution is back titrated with acid. This is because, if all the solution were to be used, the titre would be unacceptably high. Clearly an allowance must be made for this, but otherwise the calculation is exactly the same as before. This variation is featured in *Question2.*

Question 2   1.095 g of impure ammonium chloride was boiled with 20.0 cm^3 of 1.09 M NaOH(aq) until no more ammonia was evolved. The solution was then transferred to a graduated flask and made up to 250 cm^3 with distilled water. 25.0 cm^3 of this diluted solution was pipetted into a conical flask where it was titrated with 0.0973 M HCl(aq): 12.65 cm^3 were needed to reach an end-point. Calculate the percentage purity of the ammonium chloride. M_r NH$_4$Cl = 53.5

Hint   After *Step 2* an extra step is introduced to allow for the fact that only $^1/_{10}$ of the solution (i.e. 25 cm^3 out of 250 cm^3) is used in the back titration. Therefore, to find the amount of NaOH in excess in the entire 250 cm^3, the figure obtained from *Step 2* must be multiplied by ten.

Estimation Of Calcium Carbonate

Here, the reagent is hydrochloric acid:

$$CaCO_3(s) + 2HCl(aq) \rightarrow CaCl_2(aq) + CO_2(g) + H_2O(l)$$

Unless an excess of hydrochloric acid is used, it is likely that some calcium carbonate will remain undissolved; so we use a relatively large amount to ensure that it all enters solution. Bear in mind that only *part* of the HCl(aq) taken reacts with the CaCO$_3$; some is left over and is referred to as 'hydrochloric acid in excess'. This is back titrated against a standard solution of sodium hydroxide. The calculation is carried out exactly as for ammonium salts, and you should be able to answer the following question with the guidance I've provided.

Question 3   20.0 cm^3 of 1.03 M hydrochloric acid were added to 0.503 g of impure calcium carbonate, and the mixture was stirred until all the CaCO$_3$ had dissolved. The resulting solution was transferred to a 250 cm^3 volumetric flask and made up to the graduation mark with distilled water. A 25.0 cm^3 portion of this solution was neutralised by 13.0 cm^3 of 0.0980 M aqueous sodium hydroxide. Calculate the percentage purity of the calcium carbonate. M_r CaCO$_3$ = 100

Hints   Calculate: i) moles of HCl taken; ii) moles of HCl in excess in a 25 cm^3 portion of solution; iii) moles of HCl in excess in the entire 250 cm^3 of solution; iv) moles of HCl which has reacted with CaCO$_3$; v) moles of CaCO$_3$, then its mass and purity.

Answers to questions in this chapter

1. 31.9%   2. 46.4%   3. 78.1%

Chapter 13

ESTIMATION OF REDUCING AGENTS

Oxidising agents and reducing agents can be titrated against each other, just like acids and bases. The only major difference concerns the indicator. It is no use using acid-base indicators, like methyl orange or phenolphthalein; instead, *redox indicators* are generally used, although the very common potassium manganate(VII) titrations do not need an indicator at all.

Reducing agents are estimated by direct titration with standard solutions of oxidising agents, usually potassium manganate(VII) or potassium dichromate(VI). Both are used in acidic solution. Others, such as cerium(IV) sulphate, may be encountered in questions of application.

Potassium manganate(VII), $KMnO_4$, is the commonest of these oxidising agents. It is a purple coloured substance which, in acidic solution, becomes reduced to an almost colourless solution of a manganese(II) salt. It has two advantages over potassium dichromate(VI).

i.   It is a very powerful oxidising agent and can therefore be used to estimate almost any reducing agent.

ii.   Because of its intense purple colour, which shows up as a pink solution when only a trace is present, it does not require a redox indicator. Effectively, it serves as its own indicator.

Unfortunately, it also has two disadvantages.

i.   It cannot be used in the presence of Cl^- ions because it may oxidise them to chlorine. This would lead to an *over-titration*, i.e. too much $KMnO_4(aq)$ would be used. (That is why solutions to be titrated are always acidified with dilute sulphuric acid; not hydrochloric acid.)

ii.   Because it slowly decomposes on standing, it is unsuitable as a primary standard. Consequently, its solutions must be standardised before use, an aspect we shall study shortly.

Potassium dichromate(VI), $K_2Cr_2O_7$, an orange coloured substance, becomes reduced to green chromium(III) salts. Its advantages over $KMnO_4$ are:

i.   it is acceptable as a primary standard. This means that a solution does not have to be standardised before use; we simply calculate its molarity from the mass of solid which is weighed out;

ii.   it can be used in the presence of Cl^- ions because it is insufficiently powerful to oxidise them to chlorine.

There are also two disadvantages.

i.   Because it is less powerful than $KMnO_4$, it can oxidise fewer reducing agents, i.e. it is less versatile.

ii.   A redox indicator is required.

It is well worthwhile memorising these advantages and disadvantages because they commonly feature in examination questions.

Whichever of these oxidising agents is used, the calculation of results is exactly the same as for acid-base titrations. The only difference comes at the start, where, instead of stating the mole ratio of acid to base, you inspect the equation and write down the mole ratio of oxidant to reductant:

$$\frac{\text{moles of oxidant}}{\text{moles of reductant}} = \frac{x}{y} \qquad \textit{Equation 1}$$

This may be rewritten as:

$$\frac{\text{molarity} \times \text{volume (in dm}^3) \text{ of oxidant}}{\text{molarity} \times \text{volume (in dm}^3) \text{ of reductant}} = \frac{x}{y} \qquad \textit{Equation 2}$$

Bear in mind that the substitution, for moles, of molarity $\times$ volume does not necessarily have to be made in both the numerator and denominator.

Notes

1   In this book the term *oxidant* is used to denote the *chemical species* (i.e. atom, molecule or ion) which is actually responsible for the oxidation. Thus, in the case of $KMnO_4$, the oxidant is the manganate(VII) ion, MnO_4^-. (The oxidising ability of $KMnO_4$ owes nothing to K^+, which is merely a spectator ion.) The term *oxidising agent* refers to the *substance* which is used in the laboratory; here, $KMnO_4$. In some cases, e.g. Cl_2, the oxidising agent is also the oxidant.

2   Similarly, the term *reductant* is used to denote a chemical species which causes reduction, while a *reducing agent* is the substance which provides that species. Zinc, Zn, is both a reducing agent and a reductant, but sodium sulphite, Na_2SO_3, is a reducing agent which acts as a source of the reductant SO_3^{2-}, the sulphite ion.

3   **It is absolutely essential to learn what happens to the common oxidants and reductants when they do their job;** i.e. you must know the species to which oxidants become reduced and those to which reductants become oxidised. *You cannot write equations or do calculations without this information, and it is unwise to rely on the examiner providing it!*

Redox Equations

The essence of any oxidation-reduction or *redox* reaction is electron transfer from one species to another. Thus, one species loses electrons and is said to become oxidised, while the other gains electrons and is said to be reduced. If you have ever heard of an oil rig you will never forget this!

Oxidation **I**s **L**oss of electrons
Reduction **I**s **G**ain of electrons

The whole redox reaction therefore comprises two *half-reactions*, an oxidation and a reduction, for each of which we can write an *ionic half-equation*. **When constructing half-equations, you must always balance the elements first and then the electrical charges.** It is very difficult to do both at once, and you certainly cannot do it the other way round!

Ionic half-equations for reactions in neutral solution

Begin by writing down the formulae of the oxidant or reductant on the left hand side, and that of the species to which it is converted on the right hand side. For example, for chlorine behaving as an oxidant, becoming reduced to chloride ions, you must write:

$$Cl_2 \;\rightarrow\; Cl^-$$

Balance the elements if necessary: $$Cl_2 \;\rightarrow\; 2Cl^-$$

Finally, balance the charges. Ask yourself, "How many electrons are needed, and on which side of the equation must they go?" Here: $\quad Cl_2 + 2e^- \rightarrow 2Cl^-$

This gives a balance of two negative charges on both sides of the equation. Notice that chlorine is *gaining* electrons, which is in accordance with it becoming reduced.

Questions Write ionic half-equations for the following changes in neutral solution.

1 The reduction of iron(III) ions, Fe^{3+}, to iron(II) ions, Fe^{2+}.
2 The oxidation of ethanedioate ions, $C_2O_4^{2-}$, to molecules of carbon dioxide, CO_2.
3 The oxidation of iodide ions, I^-, to molecules of iodine, I_2.

Ionic half-equations for reactions in acidic solution
　　Most redox reactions occur in acidic solution, in which case you will probably need to introduce hydrogen ions, H^+, and water molecules, H_2O, on different sides of the half-equation in order to make the elements balance. **NO OTHER SPECIES CAN BE USED FOR THIS PURPOSE.** For example, for manganate(VII) ions becoming reduced to manganese(II) ions, start by writing:
$$MnO_4^- \rightarrow Mn^{2+}$$

Then balance oxygen by adding H_2O molecules to the appropriate side:

$$MnO_4^- \rightarrow Mn^{2+} + 4H_2O$$

Now balance hydrogen by adding H^+ ions to the other side:

$$MnO_4^- + 8H^+ \rightarrow Mn^{2+} + 4H_2O$$

　　Finally, balance the charges by introducing electrons. As things stand, there is a charge of 2+ on the right hand side and a net charge of 7+ on the left. We therefore need five negative charges (from five electrons) on the left hand side:

$$MnO_4^- + 8H^+ + 5e^- \rightarrow Mn^{2+} + 4H_2O$$

Questions Write ionic half-equations for the following changes in acidic solution.

4 The reduction of dichromate(VI) ions, $Cr_2O_7^{2-}$, to chromium(III) ions, Cr^{3+}. (*Hint* When balancing the elements, tackle chromium first, then oxygen and finally hydrogen.)
5 The oxidation of sulphite ions, SO_3^{2-}, to sulphate ions, SO_4^{2-}.
6 The oxidation of molecules of hydrogen peroxide, H_2O_2, to molecules of oxygen, O_2.

Complete ionic equations
　　To obtain the complete equation for a redox reaction, all you have to do is to add together the two ionic half-equations. **As you do so, you must make sure that the electrons cancel out.** Redox changes neither begin nor finish with free electrons.

　　For example, for the oxidation of iron(II) ions by manganate(VII) ions in acidic solution the half-equations are:

$$MnO_4^- + 8H^+ + 5e^- \rightarrow Mn^{2+} + 4H_2O \qquad \text{(A)}$$

$$Fe^{2+} \rightarrow Fe^{3+} + e^- \qquad \text{(B)}$$

To get the complete ionic equation we must therefore multiply half-equation (B) throughout by 5 (which gives us five electrons) and then add it to (A):

$$MnO_4^- + 8H^+ + 5Fe^{2+} \rightarrow Mn^{2+} + 4H_2O + 5Fe^{3+}$$

These ionic equations are extremely important because they show you the mole ratio of oxidant to reductant. This one, for example, tells you that:

$$\frac{\text{moles of } MnO_4^-}{\text{moles of } Fe^{2+}} = \frac{1}{5} \qquad \qquad \textit{Equation 3}$$

or

$$\frac{\text{molarity} \times \text{volume (in dm}^3\text{) of } MnO_4^-}{\text{molarity} \times \text{volume (in dm}^3\text{) of } Fe^{2+}} = \frac{1}{5} \qquad \textit{Equation 4}$$

Given this information, you should have no trouble at all with calculations, *but without the mole ratio you cannot proceed.* Practice is therefore essential.

Questions Write complete ionic equations for the following redox reactions in acidic solution.
Hint Begin by writing two ionic half-equations, and then combine them. Never attempt the "short-cut" of balancing the equation by inspection, because you'll almost certainly find that it won't be a short-cut at all!

7	The oxidation of iron(II) ions by dichromate(VI) ions.	(Refer to *Question 4.*)
8	The oxidation of ethanedioate ions by manganate(VII) ions.	(Refer to *Question 2.*)
9	The oxidation of sulphite ions by dichromate(VI) ions.	(Refer to *Question 5.*)
10	The oxidation of iodide ions by manganate(VII) ions.	(Refer to *Question 3.*)
11	The oxidation of hydrogen peroxide by manganate(VII) ions.	(Refer to *Question 6.*)

Standardisation Of Potassium Manganate(VII) Solutions

The primary standards commonly used for this purpose are ammonium iron(II) sulphate, $FeSO_4.(NH_4)_2SO_4.6H_2O$, which acts as a source of iron(II) ions, and sodium ethanedioate, $Na_2C_2O_4$, or ethanedioic acid dihydrate, $H_2C_2O_4.2H_2O$, both of which provide ethanedioate ions.

Example 10.00 g of ammonium iron(II) sulphate hexahydrate were dissolved in distilled water and the solution made up to 250 cm^3. 25.0 cm^3 of this solution were acidified with dilute sulphuric acid and titrated by 26.0 cm^3 of $KMnO_4$(aq). Calculate the molarity of the latter.
M_r $FeSO_4.(NH_4)_2SO_4.6H_2O = 392$

Work out the concentration of the ammonium iron(II) sulphate in g dm^{-3} and then mol dm^{-3}. Please do it, and check that you get the correct figure of 0.102 M.

Now write down *Equation 4,* substitute in it and calculate the required molarity. (Your answer should come to 0.0195 M.)

Question 12 1.497 g of ethanedioic acid dihydrate were dissolved in water to make 250 cm^3 of solution. 25.0 cm^3 of this solution were acidified with sulphuric acid and titrated at 70 °C by 24.6 cm^3 of $KMnO_4$(aq). Calculate the molarity of the latter. M_r $H_2C_2O_4.2H_2O = 126$
Hints Refer to *Question 8*. Temperature is not required for calculation purposes. The information is included because the reaction between MnO_4^- and $C_2O_4^{2-}$ ions will not take place at temperatures below 70 °C. Don't forget that *you* have to find the molarity of the ethanedioic acid dihydrate via its concentration in g dm^{-3}.

Applications

All the applications of acid-base titrations can be re-encountered here, including questions on diluted solutions, water of crystallisation and percentage purity. In all cases your approach should be:

i. write down ionic half-equations;
ii. combine them into a complete ionic equation;
iii. write down the mole ratio of oxidant:reductant in the style of *Equation 1* or *2* (p. 65);
iv. proceed as described for acid-base examples (*Chapter 11).*

Straightforward questions

13   0.412 g of potassium iodide were dissolved in water. The solution was acidified and then titrated against 0.0200 M $KMnO_4(aq)$. What volume of the latter was required? M_r KI = 166
Hint Refer to *Question 10.*

14   1.75 g of iron(II) ethanedioate, FeC_2O_4, were dissolved in water and made up to 250 cm^3. Acidified 25.0 cm^3 portions were then titrated against 0.0200 M $KMnO_4(aq)$. What volume of the latter was required,
a) in a titration at 20 $^\circ$C?
b) in a titration at 70 $^\circ$C?
M_r FeC_2O_4 = 144
Hints Iron(II) ethanedioate dissociates in solution:

$$FeC_2O_4(s) \ + \ aq \ \rightleftharpoons \ Fe^{2+}(aq) \ + \ C_2O_4^{2-}(aq)$$

At 20 $^\circ$C, only the Fe^{2+} ions are oxidised by MnO_4^-. Refer to *Equation 3* (p. 67).

At 70 $^\circ$C, both the Fe^{2+} and $C_2O_4^{2-}$ ions are oxidised. *Either* calculate the volume of $KMnO_4(aq)$ required to oxidise $C_2O_4^{2-}$ ions (refer to *Question 8*), and add this volume to that calculated in a), *or* write:

$$MnO_4^- \ + \ 8H^+ \ + \ 5e^- \ \rightarrow \ Mn^{2+} \ + \ 4H_2O \qquad\qquad \text{(A)}$$

$$Fe^{2+} \ C_2O_4^{2-} \ \rightarrow \ Fe^{3+} \ + \ 2CO_2 \ + \ 3e^- \qquad\qquad \text{(B)}$$

Multiply (A) by 3 and (B) by 5; then add them together:

$$3MnO_4^- \ + \ 24H^+ \ + \ 5FeC_2O_4 \ \rightarrow \ 3Mn^{2+} \ + \ 12H_2O \ + \ 5Fe^{3+} \ + \ 10CO_2$$

$\therefore$ $\qquad\qquad\qquad\qquad$ $\dfrac{\text{moles } MnO_4^-}{\text{moles } FeC_2O_4} = \dfrac{3}{5}$ $\qquad\qquad$ *Equation 5*

Dilution questions

15   25.0 cm^3 of aqueous hydrogen peroxide were diluted to 500 cm^3 with distilled water. 25.0 cm^3 of the latter were acidified and titrated by 23.7 cm^3 of 0.0198 M $KMnO_4(aq)$. Calculate the concentration, in g dm^{-3}, of the original hydrogen peroxide solution. M_r H_2O_2 = 34
Hints First calculate the molarity of the diluted solution; refer to *Question 11*. Then use a scaling-up factor (p58) to find the molarity of the original solution. Finally convert from mol dm^{-3} to g dm^{-3}.

Water of crystallisation questions

16   0.165 g of hydrated iron(II) ethanedioate, $FeC_2O_4.nH_2O$, was dissolved in distilled water. The solution, after acidification, was titrated at 70 $^\circ$C by 27.5 cm^3 of 0.0200 M $KMnO_4(aq)$. Calculate the value of n. M_r FeC_2O_4 = 144; M_r H_2O = 18
Hints First calculate the number of moles of anhydrous FeC_2O_4, using *Equation 5*; then its mass. Next

get the mass of H_2O by subtracting the mass of anhydrous FeC_2O_4 from that of the hydrated compound (0.165 g). Finally, find the moles of H_2O and hence the mole ratio of $FeC_2O_4 : H_2O$.

Content and purity calculations

17   A brand of 'lawn sand', to control moss in lawns, contains iron(II) sulphate heptahydrate, $FeSO_4.7H_2O$. 2.69 g of lawn sand were added to distilled water and shaken for long enough to allow the iron(II) sulphate to dissolve. After acidification, the mixture was titrated with 24.0 cm³ of 0.0200 M $KMnO_4(aq)$. Calculate the percentages of a) Fe, b) $FeSO_4$ and c) $FeSO_4.7H_2O$ in the lawn sand. A_r Fe = 56; M_r $FeSO_4$ = 152; M_r $FeSO_4.7H_2O$ = 278
Hints Refer to *Equation 3* (p. 67) and acid-base percentage purity calculations (*Chapter 11*).

18   1.37 g of mild steel (an alloy of iron and carbon) were dissolved in dilute sulphuric acid, so that iron entered solution as iron(II) sulphate. (The carbon did not dissolve.) The solution was made up to 250 cm³, after which 25.0 cm³ were titrated with 24.2 cm³ of 0.0167 M $K_2Cr_2O_7(aq)$. Calculate the percentage of iron in the mild steel. A_r Fe = 56. *Hint* Refer to *Question 7*.

19   Hamburgers may contain sodium sulphite, Na_2SO_3, as a preservative. An analyst, checking on the quality of a "quarterpounder", extracted the sodium sulphite with water and titrated the acidified extract with 20.7 cm³ of 0.003 M $K_2Cr_2O_7(aq)$. Calculate the mass of Na_2SO_3 in the quarterpounder. M_r Na_2SO_3 = 126. *Hint* Refer to *Question 9*.

Capacity Of Oxidising Agents

For most of the above applications, $KMnO_4$ or $K_2Cr_2O_7$ can equally well be used as the oxidising agent. In the examination you may be asked about the consequences of switching from one to the other. If you look at the two ionic half-equations,

$$MnO_4^- + 8H^+ + 5e^- \rightarrow Mn^{2+} + 4H_2O$$
$$Cr_2O_7^{2-} + 14H^+ + 6e^- \rightarrow 2Cr^{3+} + 7H_2O$$

you will see that whereas one mole of MnO_4^- ions accepts five moles of electrons, one mole of $Cr_2O_7^{2-}$ ions will accept *six*. It follows that the dichromate(VI) has a greater *oxidising capacity* than the manganate(VII), i.e. 1 mol of $K_2Cr_2O_7$ will oxidise more reducing agent than 1 mol of $KMnO_4$. If, therefore, we were to switch from $KMnO_4$ to $K_2Cr_2O_7$, we should need only $^5/_6$ as much oxidising agent. This means that, if the molarities of the two oxidising agents were the same, we could use a smaller volume ($^5/_6$) of $K_2Cr_2O_7$ solution; alternatively, if the volumes were to remain equal, the molarity of the $K_2Cr_2O_7$ would be less than that of the $KMnO_4$ - again by a factor of $^5/_6$.

Question 20   30.0 cm³ of an iron(II) sulphate solution was titrated by 25.0 cm³ of 0.02 M $KMnO_4(aq)$. If the $KMnO_4(aq)$ were to be replaced by $K_2Cr_2O_7(aq)$,
a)   what volume of 0.02 M $K_2Cr_2O_7(aq)$ would be required?
b)   what would be the molarity of the $K_2Cr_2O_7(aq)$ if 25.0 cm³ were needed for the titration?
Hint Disregard the volume of $FeSO_4(aq)$. Never feel obliged to use all the data provided by an examiner.

Caution! Do be careful not to confuse the *capacity* of an oxidising agent, i.e. how much oxidation it will bring about, with its *oxidising power*. Oxidising agents (and reducing agents) vary enormously in their power, ranging from the extremely powerful (and hence dangerous) to the downright feeble, and a measure of this is provided by the standard electrode potential ($E^{\ominus}$ value). Although the topic is beyond the scope of this book, it is worth noting that, although $K_2Cr_2O_7$ has a greater oxidising capacity than $KMnO_4$, it is nevertheless a weaker oxidising agent.

Answers to questions in this chapter

1. $Fe^{3+} + e^- \rightarrow Fe^{2+}$
2. $C_2O_4^{2-} \rightarrow 2CO_2 + 2e^-$
3. $2I^- \rightarrow I_2 + 2e^-$
4. $Cr_2O_7^{2-} + 14H^+ + 6e^- \rightarrow 2Cr^{3+} + 7H_2O$
5. $SO_3^{2-} + H_2O \rightarrow SO_4^{2-} + 2H^+ + 2e^-$
6. $H_2O_2 \rightarrow O_2 + 2H^+ + 2e^-$
7. $Cr_2O_7^{2-} + 6Fe^{2+} + 14H^+ \rightarrow 2Cr^{3+} + 6Fe^{3+} + 7H_2O$
8. $2MnO_4^- + 5C_2O_4^{2-} + 16H^+ \rightarrow 2Mn^{2+} + 10CO_2 + 8H_2O$
9. $Cr_2O_7^{2-} + 3SO_3^{2-} + 8H^+ \rightarrow 2Cr^{3+} + 3SO_4^{2-} + 4H_2O$
10. $2MnO_4^- + 10I^- + 16H^+ \rightarrow 2Mn^{2+} + 5I_2 + 8H_2O$
11. $2MnO_4^- + 5H_2O_2 + 6H^+ \rightarrow 2Mn^{2+} + 5O_2 + 8H_2O$
12. 0.0193 M
13. 24.8 cm^3
14. a) 12.15 cm^3 b) 36.45 cm^3
15. 31.9 g dm^{-3}
16. 2
17. a) 5.00% b) 13.6% c) 24.8%
18. 99.1%
19. 0.0235 g
20. a) 20.8 cm^3 b) 0.0167 M

Chapter 14

ESTIMATION OF OXIDISING AGENTS

You may or may not have met this topic before; but let's suppose you haven't, and you are asked how you would estimate a solution of an oxidising agent. You'd probably say, "Easy. Just titrate it with a reducing agent." This is by no means a daft suggestion. You could certainly prepare a standard solution of a reducing agent, such as iron(II) sulphate, tin(II) chloride or sodium sulphite and, with a redox indicator, carry out a direct titration. A chemist, however, would not be entirely happy about the accuracy of the result. It *may* be all right, but nevertheless there would be uncertainty because of the unreliability of many reducing agents. They deteriorate on standing or, as we say in Birmingham, they "go orf".

The trouble is that we live and work in an oxidising environment. Oxygen of the air slowly oxidises iron(II) salts to iron(III) salts, tin(II) compounds to those of tin(IV), sulphites to sulphates, etc, so that we can never be entirely sure of the concentration of a solution. I once asked students how they would overcome the problem, and one lad suggested working in a non-oxidising atmosphere. "Excellent idea," I said, "go away and try it." Do you know, he never came back. So there must be some unfortunate consequences; like death! Seriously, though, this *can* be done, by placing the apparatus in a 'nitrogen box' (a chamber through which nitrogen gas is passing) and operating the apparatus from the outside. However, this is inconvenient and seldom attempted.

Direct titration can be carried out only when the reducing agent is resistant to aerial oxidation. The best example is sodium ethanedioate, used in the standardisation of solutions of potassium manganate(VII). Unfortunately, such reducing agents, because they are difficult to oxidise, have very few applications and can only be used to titrate powerful oxidising agents. All others must be estimated by one of the following techniques.

Complete Reduction Followed By Titration With $KMnO_4$(aq) Or $K_2Cr_2O_7$(aq)

This method is generally used for the estimation of iron(III) salts. A certain volume of the iron(III) solution is pipetted into a conical flask, dilute sulphuric acid and zinc are added, and the flask is boiled for about 15-20 minutes. To ensure that reduction is complete, a drop of solution is removed on the end of a glass rod and tested with a solution of potassium thiocyanate, KSCN(aq): if a blood red colour develops we know that reduction is incomplete and a little more boiling is required. Excess zinc is then filtered off, and the filtrate (now containing iron in the form of Fe^{2+} ions) is titrated with a standard solution of $KMnO_4$ or $K_2Cr_2O_7$ in the usual way.

Working out the results is very easy, because the iron(III) is reduced to iron(II) according to the half-equation

$$Fe^{3+}(aq) + e^- \rightarrow Fe^{2+}(aq)$$

Consequently, the concentration of iron(II) ions in the reduced solution is equal to that of iron(III) ions in the original solution.

Question 1 12.8 g of iron alum were dissolved in water and the solution made up to 250 cm^3. 25.0 cm^3 of this solution were completely reduced with zinc and dilute sulphuric acid and then (after removal of the excess zinc) titrated with 26.0 cm^3 of 0.0196 M $KMnO_4$(aq). Calculate the percentage of iron in iron alum. A_r Fe = 56

Although, in principle, the method can be applied to all sorts of oxidising agents, in practice it is restricted to iron(III) compounds. The difficulty lies in ensuring that reduction is complete. In the case of iron(III) there is no trouble, because potassium thiocyanate provides a very sensitive test for the presence of Fe^{3+} ions, but for other oxidants corresponding reagents are simply not available.

Iodimetry

In view of the limitations of the previous method, another one is clearly needed. This is provided by *iodimetry*, which is so versatile that virtually any oxidising agent can be estimated in this way. The technique involves pipetting a certain volume of the aqueous oxidising agent into a conical flask, acidifying the solution with dilute hydrochloric or sulphuric acid, and adding an excess of potassium iodide solution. A redox reaction occurs, in which the oxidant converts iodide ions into iodine. (Almost any oxidant will do this; hence the versatility of the method.) Because the oxidant is deficient, it controls the yield of iodine. The amount of iodine liberated is then estimated by titration with a standard solution of sodium thiosulphate.

You must understand the reaction between molecular iodine and thiosulphate ions. It is a redox change in which iodine behaves as the oxidising agent, converting thiosulphate ions, $S_2O_3^{2-}$, to tetrathionate ions, $S_4O_6^{2-}$:

$$2S_2O_3^{2-} \rightarrow S_4O_6^{2-} + 2e^-$$

$$I_2 + 2e^- \rightarrow 2I^-$$

Hence: $\qquad\qquad 2S_2O_3^{2-} + I_2 \rightarrow S_4O_6^{2-} + 2I^- \qquad\qquad$ *Equation 1*

This is a rather surprising reaction because iodine is a very weak oxidising agent and seldom behaves in this way.

A redox indicator is not required because the dark brown colour of the iodine is gradually discharged (through various shades of brown and yellow) during the titration and, in principle, all we have to do is to watch for the point where the last trace of yellow colour disappears. In practice, however, this is a very difficult change to observe, and freshly prepared starch solution is added near the end-point. This converts residual iodine to an iodine-starch complex, which imparts an intense blue-black colour to the solution. When further sodium thiosulphate solution is run in from the burette, it is easy to see this very dark colour disappear sharply at the end-point.

Calculating results - the long way!

Although iodimetry is an easy and accurate laboratory method, the calculation of results may seem difficult. A short cut can usually be taken but, before looking at this, we must study the calculation in full because this is sometimes needed in examinations.

Always keep the underlying chemistry in mind. The amount of oxidant that we start with controls the amount of iodine which is liberated: this in turn governs the amount of thiosulphate used in the titration:

$$x \text{ mol oxidant} \equiv y \text{ mol } I_2 \equiv z \text{ mol } S_2O_3^{2-}$$

In the calculation we must begin, as always, with the experimental results. From the molarity and volume of $Na_2S_2O_3(aq)$ we can calculate the amount of $S_2O_3^{2-}$ (z mol). We can then relate this to the amount of I_2 (y mol): reference to *Equation 1* (above) shows that y will be $\frac{1}{2}z$. Finally, by referring to the equation for the reaction between the oxidant and I^- ions, we can estimate how much oxidant was present in the original solution.

Example   25.0 cm^3 of potassium dichromate(VI) solution were acidified and treated with excess KI(aq). The liberated iodine was titrated with 24.4 cm^3 of 0.102 M Na$_2$S$_2$O$_3$(aq). Calculate the molarity of the K$_2$Cr$_2$O$_7$(aq).

Remember, this is a three stage calculation. Let's work through it together.

Stage 1   Calculate the amount (in mol) of Na$_2$S$_2$O$_3$. Please do it! (It should be 2.49 × 10^{-3} mol.)

Stage 2   Refer to *Equation 1* and calculate the amount of I$_2$. (1.24 × 10^{-3} mol.)

Stage 3   Write the equation for the reaction between Cr$_2$O$_7^{2-}$ and I$^-$ ions:

$$Cr_2O_7^{2-} + 14H^+ + 6e^- \rightarrow 2Cr^{3+} + 7H_2O$$

$$2I^- \rightarrow I_2 + 2e^- \qquad (\times 3)$$

Add: $\qquad Cr_2O_7^{2-} + 14H^+ + 6I^- \rightarrow 2Cr^{3+} + 7H_2O + 3I_2 \qquad$ *Equation 2*

Inspect this equation and write down the amount of Cr$_2$O$_7^{2-}$ ions; hence K$_2$Cr$_2$O$_7$. **Bear in mind that this is moles in 25 cm^3.** Finally calculate the molarity of the K$_2$Cr$_2$O$_7$. (0.0166 M)

Calculating results - a short cut

Unless you are specifically asked to calculate moles of I$_2$, you can save valuable time by omitting the iodine and simply relating the amount of oxidant to the amount of thiosulphate used in the titration. Let's go back to the last example.

$$x\, Cr_2O_7^{2-} \equiv y\, I_2 \equiv z\, S_2O_3^{2-}$$

Logic dictates that if *x* is equivalent to *y*, and *y* in turn is equivalent to *z*, then *x* and *z* are equivalent to each other,

i.e. $\qquad\qquad\qquad x\, Cr_2O_7^{2-} \equiv z\, S_2O_3^{2-}$

We can rewrite this:

$$\frac{\text{moles of } Cr_2O_7^{2-}}{\text{moles of } S_2O_3^{2-}} = \frac{x}{z}$$

The ratio *x/z* is easily found by inspecting the chemical equations.

Equation 2 shows that 1 mol Cr$_2$O$_7^{2-}$ ≡ 3 mol I$_2$

Equation 1 shows that 3 mol I$_2$ ≡ 6 mol S$_2$O$_3^{2-}$

To summarise, 1Cr$_2$O$_7^{2-}$ ≡ 3I$_2$ ≡ 6S$_2$O$_3^{2-}$

∴ $$\frac{\text{moles of } Cr_2O_7^{2-}}{\text{moles of } S_2O_3^{2-}} = \frac{1}{6}$$

∴ $$\frac{\text{molarity} \times \text{volume (in dm}^3) \, Cr_2O_7^{2-}}{\text{molarity} \times \text{volume (in dm}^3) \, S_2O_3^{2-}} = \frac{1}{6}$$

Substituting figures in this equation gives:

$$\frac{M(Cr_2O_7^{2-}) \times 0.025}{0.102 \times 0.0244} = \frac{1}{6}$$

which, on working out, gives the same answer as before.

The method is of general application. Always begin by constructing the ionic equation for the reaction between the given oxidant and I^- ions. (If you're lucky, the examiner will give you this!) Then write down:

$$\frac{\text{moles of oxidant}}{\text{moles of } S_2O_3^{2-}} = \frac{x}{z}$$

Inspect your ionic equation and *Equation 1* to find the value of the ratio x/z; finally, substitute given figures and calculate whatever is unknown.

Questions
2   25.0 cm³ of KMnO₄(aq) were acidified with dilute H₂SO₄; excess KI(aq) was added, and the liberated I₂ titrated by 25.1 cm³ of 0.099 M Na₂S₂O₃(aq). Calculate the molar concentration of the KMnO₄(aq). *Hint* Refer to the ionic half-equation for MnO₄⁻ reduction on p. 66.
3   0.625 g of commercial CuSO₄.5H₂O crystals were dissolved in distilled water, acidified and treated with excess KI(aq). The liberated I₂ required 24.8 cm³ of 0.100 M Na₂S₂O₃(aq) in a titration with starch indicator. Calculate the percentage purity of the copper sulphate crystals.
M_r CuSO₄.5H₂O = 249.5
Hints The ionic equation for the redox reaction between Cu²⁺ and I⁻ ions is as follows:

$$2Cu^{2+}(aq) \ + \ 4I^-(aq) \ \rightarrow \ 2CuI(s) \ + \ I_2(aq)$$

Calculate mol Cu²⁺ and hence mol CuSO₄.5H₂O. (The two are numerically equal.)

4   In an experiment to determine the concentration of sodium chlorate(I), NaClO, in a supermarket disinfectant, 15.0 cm³ of disinfectant were diluted to 250 cm³ in a graduated flask. 25.0 cm³ of the diluted solution were acidified, treated with excess KI(aq) and titrated against 0.100 M Na₂S₂O₃(aq) with starch as the indicator: 23.0 cm³ were required. Calculate a) the molarity of the diluted solution, and b) the mass concentration of the original disinfectant. M_r NaClO = 74.5
Hint The ionic half-equation for the reduction of chlorate(I) ions in acidic solution is:

$$ClO^- \ + \ 2H^+ \ + \ 2e^- \ \rightarrow \ Cl^- \ + \ H_2O$$

Standardisation of sodium thiosulphate solutions
As a volumetric reagent, sodium thiosulphate suffers from the same disadvantage as potassium manganate(VII), namely that solutions tend to deteriorate on standing and therefore need to be standardised before use. The question is, "How?" The answer is, "By iodimetry, using exactly the same procedure as before." You may think this is silly, because we are apparently going round in a circle, but if we start with a *reliable* oxidising agent this is not so. Quite simply, instead of using Na₂S₂O₃ to estimate an oxidising agent, we use an oxidising agent to estimate Na₂S₂O₃: the technique and calculation remain unaltered.

There are several oxidising agents which are acceptable as primary standards. The ones most commonly used are potassium iodate(V), KIO₃, and its baby brother, KBrO₃. Others include K₂Cr₂O₇ and CuSO₄.5H₂O.

Question 5 0.938 g of potassium iodate(V) was weighed out, dissolved in distilled water and made up to 250 cm^3. 25.0 cm^3 of this solution, after acidification and the addition of excess KI(aq), were titrated by 26.7 cm^3 of Na$_2$S$_2$O$_3$(aq). Calculate the molarity of the latter. M_r KIO$_3$ = 214

Hints The ionic half-equation for the reduction of iodate(V) ions in acidic solution is:

$$IO_3^- \; + \; 6H^+ \; + \; 6e^- \; \rightarrow \; I^- \; + \; 3H_2O$$

Notice that it *your* job to work out the molarity of the KIO$_3$ solution before tackling the main calculation.

Answers to questions in this chapter

1. 11.1%   2. 0.0199 M   3. 99.0%   4. a) 0.0460 M   b) 57.1 g dm^{-3} 5. 0.0985 M

Chapter 15

SILVER NITRATE TITRATIONS

I should like to begin this chapter by asking you a simple question. "What volumetric reagent and indicator would you use to estimate chloride ions in solution?" Do think about it and, if possible, jot down the answer before reading any further.

If you have said, "Titrate with sodium hydroxide solution, with methyl orange or phenolphthalein as the indicator," you would be in good company because this is what most 'A' level students say, but at the same time you would be completely wrong! Sodium hydroxide does not react with ionic chlorides, such as sodium chloride. The misconception arises because NaOH(aq) is commonly used for estimating hydrochloric acid, which obviously contains Cl^- ions, but this is an acid-base titration in which H^+ *ions* from the HCl(aq) react with OH$^-$ ions from the NaOH(aq). Cl^- is merely a spectator ion.

The correct answer to the question is that chloride ions are estimated by titration with silver nitrate solution, using potassium chromate(VI) as an indicator. The reaction which occurs is:

$$Ag^+(aq) \ + \ Cl^-(aq) \ \rightarrow \ AgCl(s)$$

Silver nitrate solution always goes in the burette. As it is run into the chloride solution, a white precipitate of silver chloride is formed at first. Eventually, when there are no more Cl^- ions in solution, a red precipitate of silver chromate(VI) is formed instead, and this marks the end-point:

$$2Ag^+(aq) \ + \ CrO_4^{2-}(aq) \ \rightarrow \ Ag_2CrO_4(s)$$

Silver chloride is precipitated preferentially because it is less soluble than silver chromate(VI).

Silver nitrate is a light-sensitive compound which, even in dark bottles, deteriorates on standing. Solutions should be standardised before use, using pure sodium chloride as a primary standard. To work out the result, as in all calculations on this topic, you should write down the molecular equation to obtain the mole ratio of silver nitrate to the ionic chloride:

$$AgNO_3(aq) \ + \ NaCl(aq) \ \rightarrow \ AgCl(s) \ + \ NaNO_3(aq)$$

$\therefore$ $$\frac{\text{moles } AgNO_3}{\text{moles NaCl}} \ = \ \frac{1}{1}$$

Question 1 0.286 g of pure sodium chloride was weighed out and dissolved in distilled water so as to make 500 cm³ of solution. 25.0 cm³ of this solution were pipetted into a conical flask, K_2CrO_4(aq) was added as indicator, and 24.7 cm³ of AgNO$_3$(aq) were run in to reach the end-point. Calculate the molarity of the AgNO$_3$(aq). M_r NaCl = 58.5

The need to write a *molecular equation*, rather than an ionic one, is apparent when a Group 2 chloride is involved, as in the next question.

Question 2 0.780 g of the anhydrous chloride of a Group 2 element was dissolved in distilled water to make 250 cm³ of solution. 25.0 cm³ of this solution were titrated by 28.1 cm³ of 0.0500 M AgNO$_3$(aq). Calculate the relative atomic mass of the Group 2 element and hence identify it. A_r Cl = 35.5

Hints The equation is:

$$MCl_2(aq) \; + \; 2AgNO_3(aq) \; \rightarrow \; 2AgCl(s) \; + \; M(NO_3)_2(aq)$$

From the moles of $AgNO_3$ used in the titration you can find the moles of MCl_2 in 25.0 cm^3 of solution and hence in 250 cm^3. You are given the mass corresponding to this (0.780 g), so you can easily work out the M_r of the Group 2 chloride and, from that, the A_r of the metal (M).

Silver nitrate titrations must be carried out under neutral conditions. If the solution is acidic, the red precipitate of Ag_2CrO_4 does not form at the end-point, and if it is alkaline a brown precipitate of Ag_2O is produced. Acidic solutions must always be neutralised by adding a slight excess of powdered calcium carbonate; the excess $CaCO_3$ produces turbidity but does not cause alkalinity and therefore does not adversely affect the titration.

Question 3 Calculate the concentrations (in g dm^{-3}) of sodium chloride and hydrochloric acid in a mixed solution from the results of two separate titrations, in each of which 25.0 cm^3 of the mixed solution were used:
a) 23.55 cm^3 of 0.0520 M NaOH(aq) were needed, with methyl orange indicator;
b) 23.95 cm^3 of 0.102 M $AgNO_3(aq)$ were needed (after treatment with $CaCO_3$) with $K_2CrO_4(aq)$ indicator.
M_r NaCl = 58.5 M_r HCl = 36.5
Hints Titration a) gives the molarity of HCl(aq). Titration b) gives total molarity. Subtract one from the other to obtain the molarity of NaCl(aq).

Answers to questions in this chapter

1. 0.0099 M   2. 40 (calcium)   3. NaCl = 2.85 g dm^{-3}; HCl = 1.79 g dm^{-3}

Chapter 16

COMPLEXOMETRIC TITRATIONS

Salts of zinc and the Group 2 metals can be estimated by titration with the disodium salt of ethylenediaminetetraacetic acid:

$$Na^+ \ \ ^-:OOCCH_2 \qquad\qquad CH_2COO^-: \ Na^+$$
$$\diagdown \qquad\qquad \diagup$$
$$:N-CH_2-CH_2-N:$$
$$\diagup \qquad\qquad \diagdown$$
$$HOOCCH_2 \qquad\qquad CH_2COOH$$

This dissociates in solution to give the ethylenediaminetetraacetate ion (edta) which, with six lone pairs of electrons, can coordinate to metal ions in a 1:1 ratio to give a cyclic complex:

$$M^{2+} + H_2edta^{2-} \rightarrow Medta^{2-} + 2H^+$$

An indicator such as eriochrome black is used, which initially forms a coloured complex with the metal ions:

$$M^{2+} + indicator \rightarrow M\text{-indicator complex}$$
$$\text{Colour A} \qquad\qquad \text{Colour B}$$

As the $Na_2H_2edta(aq)$ is run in from the burette, metal ions transfer themselves from the M-indicator complex to the edta (which is a stronger ligand). At the end-point, when all the metal ions have been transferred, the colour of the M-indicator complex changes to that of the free indicator, i.e.

$$M\text{-indicator complex} + edta \rightarrow Medta^{2-} + indicator$$
$$\text{Colour B} \qquad\qquad\qquad \text{Colour A}$$

In questions at 'A' level you are either told to assume a 1:1 ratio for the reactions between cations and edta, or given information from which the ratio can be deduced.

Questions

1   25.0 cm³ of tap water, containing Mg^{2+} and Ca^{2+} ions, was titrated with a 0.0100 M solution of the sodium salt of edta: 19.4 cm³ of the latter were required. A further 25.0 cm³ portion of the tap water were treated with NaOH(aq), to precipitate Mg^{2+} ions as $Mg(OH)_2$, and again titrated with the 0.0100 M edta solution: this time only 13.1 cm³ were required. Calculate the parts per million (ppm) of Mg^{2+} and Ca^{2+} ions in the tap water. A_r: Mg = 24; Ca = 40.

Hints   Assume a 1:1 ratio for both Mg^{2+} and Ca^{2+} reacting with edta. Calculate, from the first titration, the total molarity of the ions; then, from the second titration, the molarity of Ca^{2+} alone. Subtraction gives the molarity of Mg^{2+}. Convert to mass concentrations, i.e. g dm⁻³, which approximates to g kg⁻¹. Finally multiply by 1000 to get ppm, i.e. g t⁻¹.

2   7.415 g of $ZnSO_4.7H_2O$ were dissolved in distilled water to make 250 cm³ of solution. 25.0 cm³ of this solution was titrated by 25.8 cm³ of 0.100 M edta solution. Calculate the mole ratio for the reaction between Zn^{2+} and edta ions. M_r $ZnSO_4.7H_2O$ = 287.4

Answers to questions in this chapter

1.   60.5 ppm Mg^{2+}, 209.6 ppm Ca^{2+} 2.   1:1

Chapter 17

HYBRID CALCULATIONS

Throughout this book I have been very careful, in each chapter, to show you calculations of one particular type. In real life, however, the situation may be more complicated. Examination questions often combine two or more types, e.g. a titration calculation coupled with one on reacting masses, or with a formula calculation. The combinations are almost endless! My advice to you must be to master simple calculations first; then, when tackling 'hybrid' ones, identify the component types and apply the principles you have learnt.

Question 1 0.102 g of commercial zinc dust was added to excess iron(III) chloride solution. The resulting iron(II) solution required 28.7 cm^3 of 0.0200 M KMnO$_4$(aq) for titration. Calculate the percentage purity of the zinc. A_r Zn = 65.4
  Hint Begin, as always with experimental data: calculate the moles of iron(II). Then do a 'reacting masses' calculation (*Chapter 10*) to find how much zinc produced the iron(II) ions in the reaction:

$$Zn(s) + 2Fe^{3+}(aq) \rightarrow Zn^{2+}(aq) + 2Fe^{2+}(aq).$$

Question 2 0.213 g of barium peroxide, BaO$_2$, were treated with dilute sulphuric acid so as to liberate hydrogen peroxide. The latter was titrated by 24.4 cm^3 of 0.0200 M KMnO$_4$(aq). Calculate the percentage purity of the BaO$_2$. M_r BaO$_2$ = 169
Hint Calculate moles of H$_2$O$_2$, then BaO$_2$. Refer to *Chapter 13, Question 11.*

Question 3 The mineral dolomite can be represented by the formula Mg$_x$Ca$_y$(CO$_3$)$_z$. From the following analytical results, calculate the values of x, y and z.
i)   A sample of dolomite was dissolved in hydrochloric acid and the solution made up to 250 cm^3 with distilled water. As the dolomite dissolved in the acid, 44.8 cm^3 of carbon dioxide (measured at s.t.p.) were evolved. (1 mole of a gas occupies 22.4 dm^3 at s.t.p.)
ii)   25.0 cm^3 of the resulting solution were titrated by 20.0 cm^3 of 0.0100 M edta solution.
iii)   Another 25.0 cm^3 portion of the solution gave a precipitate of calcium ethanedioate, CaC$_2$O$_4$, of mass 0.0128 g on treatment with aqueous ammonium ethanedioate. M_r CaC$_2$O$_4$ = 128
Hints Use the data from i) to calculate moles of CO$_3^{2-}$. Use ii) to calculate total moles of Mg^{2+} and Ca^{2+}; both react with edta in a 1:1 ratio. Use iii) to calculate moles of Ca^{2+}.

Question 4 Calculate the formula of a hydrated double salt containing NH$_4^+$, Cu^{2+} and SO$_4^{2-}$ ions from the results of the following experiments, each carried out on 1.00 g samples of the salt.
i)   One sample, on boiling with excess NaOH(aq), released ammonia which was absorbed in 50.0 cm^3 of 0.200 M HCl(aq). Back titration required 25.0 cm^3 of 0.200 M NaOH(aq).
ii)   Another sample was dissolved in water, acidified with hydrochloric acid and treated with an excess of barium chloride solution. The precipitated barium sulphate had a mass of 1.175 g.
iii)   A third sample was dissolved in water, acidified and treated with an excess of potassium iodide solution. The liberated iodine was titrated by 25.0 cm^3 of 0.100 M Na$_2$S$_2$O$_3$(aq).
A_r: H = 1; N = 14; O = 16; S = 32; Cu = 63.5; Ba = 137.
Hints From i) calculate moles of NH$_4^+$ (p. 61). From ii) calculate moles of SO$_4^{2-}$ (p. 30). From iii) calculate moles of Cu^{2+} (p. 74). Convert each of these amounts to masses, add them up and hence find mass of H$_2$O; then moles of H$_2$O. The ratio of moles gives the formula.

Answers to questions in this chapter

1. 92.0%   2. 96.8%   3. $x = 1$, $y = 1$, $z = 2$ 4. (NH$_4$)$_2$Cu(SO$_4$)$_2$.6H$_2$O

Chapter 18

WHAT EXACTLY IS A MOLE?

As you approach the end of this book, you may well be in the curious position of being able to do mole calculations without knowing exactly what a mole is. Let me remedy the deficiency now. **A mole is an amount of substance containing the same number of particles** (usually molecules) **as there are atoms in 12 grams of the isotope carbon-12.** Are you enlightened? Probably not! If you are to understand this, you must be prepared to read through the following story.

Once upon a time, there was a very small unit of mass called the *atomic mass unit* (amu), which proved very useful for expressing the masses of small particles. It was much more convenient to quote the mass of, say, a proton as 1 amu, rather than 1.67×10^{-24} g. Definitions of the amu changed over the years. Originally, it was taken to be the mass of a hydrogen atom; later $^1/_{16}$ the mass of an oxygen atom, and finally, when it was realised that it needed to be pegged to one particular nuclide, it was redefined as $^1/_{12}$ the mass of an atom of the isotope carbon-12. (Fractions were introduced to avoid changing the accepted values of atomic masses.)

In 1960 the amu had to be dropped as a mass unit because it did not conform to the Systeme International d'Unités (SI). To allow chemists to continue using traditional values of atomic and molecular masses, and to avoid having to quote them in grams, the concept of *relative mass* was introduced, defined as the number of times the mass of a particle is greater than one-twelfth the mass of a carbon-12 atom, i.e

$$\text{relative mass of a particle } = \frac{\text{mass of the particle}}{\text{one twelfth the mass of a carbon} - 12 \text{ atom}}$$

Relative mass is thus a ratio, and like all ratios is simply a number without units. Looked at another way, actual masses in any units you like (SI or non-SI) can be inserted in the above equation, but the units in numerator and denominator cancel out to give just a number.

Although the amu has no place as a mass unit in modern chemistry, it still remains a valuable abbreviation for the phrase "one-twelfth the mass of a carbon-12 atom", and it is this meaning that should be attached to 'amu' in the following discussion.

Chemists often say that although they cannot work with individual molecules (because they are far too small), they *can* work with moles: the change from one to the other is just a scaling-up process because there is a constant number of molecules in a mole. What does this mean?

Changing units is the simplest (and probably the commonest) way of scaling-up or scaling-down. Suppose a development chemist in a jam factory has produced a recipe involving 1 kg of fruit and 3 kg of sugar, and wants to transfer the recipe to production. The works manager would probably say, "Right, let's scale it up; say, 1 t of fruit and 3 t of sugar." This corresponds to multiplication by 1000, i.e. the number of kilograms in a tonne. In the same way, the change from a molecule to a mole involves multiplication by a factor of 6.023×10^{23}, known as the *Avogadro constant, L,* corresponding to the number of molecules (or other particles) in a mole.

For carbon -12 atoms,

$$1\ ^{12}\text{C atom} \xrightarrow{\times L} 1\ \text{mol}\ ^{12}\text{C atoms}$$

mass   12 amu   12g

Hence, **L is the number of atoms in 12g of carbon -12**, which is the generally accepted definition of the Avogadro constant.

The same is true of substances other than carbon-12. Whenever we switch from a molecule (or atom, in the case of certain elements) to a mole, we multiply by a factor of L. Thus, there are always L molecules (or atoms, as the case may be) in a mole. **A mole can therefore be defined as an amount of substance containing the number of particles equal to the Avogadro constant.**